25·8–25·10 Sex can lead to fertilization, but it can also spread sexually transmitted diseases.

Organisms can reproduce sexually or asexually—or both.

FERTILIZATION

It's not enough for sperm cells to be in the same general location as an egg—there are some specific events that must occur for fertilization.

1 PENETRATION
A sperm pushes its way through the granulosa cells, and enzymes within its acrosome digest the zona pellucida.

2 ACTIVATION
The plasma membrane of the sperm and egg fuse, making it impossible for other sperm to fuse with the egg.

3 NUCLEI FUSION
The haploid nucleus of the egg fuses with the haploid nucleus of the sperm, forming a diploid zygote.

METHODS OF CONTRACEPTION

Pregnancy can be prevented by numerous methods, each of which acts in one or more ways to prevent ovulation, fertilization, or implantation.

PREVENTING OVULATION
- Birth control pills
- Hormone injections or implants

PREVENTING FERTILIZATION
- Condoms
- Diaphragm/cervical cap
- Sterilization
- Abstinence

PREVENTING IMPLANTATION
- Intrauterine device (IUD)
- "Morning-after" pills

SEXUALLY TRANSMITTED DISEASES

Sexually transmitted diseases (STDs) are caused by a variety of organisms, including bacteria, viruses, protists, fungi, and arthropods. Worldwide, more than 300 million people are infected each year. The symptoms of STDs range from nonexistent to mild to extreme discomfort, sterility, or even death.

25·11–25·14 Human development occurs in specific stages.

How does a complex organism develop from a single cell?

EARLY EMBRYONIC DEVELOPMENT

The structures of the male reproductive system.

CLEAVAGE
Soon after fertilization, cleavage takes place, and many rapid cell divisions occur without overall growth.

GASTRULATION
In gastrulation, a gut begins to form, along with three distinct germ layers with specific developmental fates.

NEURULATION
In neurulation, mesoderm forms a supporting rod called the notochord, and above that, an infolding of ectoderm forms a neural tube, which will become the brain and spinal cord.

SEX DIFFERENTIATION

Mammalian embryos develop female internal and external reproductive organs unless a gene on the Y chromosome stimulates fetal gonads to develop as testes, leading to testosterone production, which then stimulates the development of male reproductive organs.

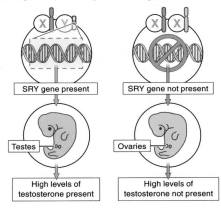

SRY gene present | SRY gene not present

Testes | Ovaries

High levels of testosterone present | High levels of testosterone not present

HUMAN EMBRYO AND FETUS DEVELOPMENT

The nine months of human fetal development are divided into three-month trimesters.

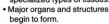

FIRST TRIMESTER: MONTHS 1–3
- Cells begin to differentiate into specialized types of tissues.
- Major organs and structures begin to form.

SECOND TRIMESTER: MONTHS 4–6
- Significant muscle and bone growth occurs, with less new development relative to the first trimester.

THIRD TRIMESTER: MONTHS 7–9
- Significant development of the nervous system takes place.

25·15 Reproductive technology has benefits and dangers.

Many methods exist that help otherwise infertile couples have children.

ASSISTED REPRODUCTIVE TECHNOLOGY (ART) METHODS

Assisted reproductive technology (ART) procedures typically involve removing eggs from a woman's ovaries, combining them with sperm to achieve fertilization, and reinserting the fertilized eggs into the woman's uterus or Fallopian tube. These technologies can enable previously infertile couples to have babies.

IN VITRO FERTILIZATION-EMBRYO TRANSFER (IVF–ET)

Eggs are combined with sperm in a Petri dish, where fertilization occurs.

Fertilized eggs at the 8-cell stage are inserted into the uterus.

ZYGOTE INTRA-FALLOPIAN TUBE TRANSFER (ZIFT)

Eggs are combined with sperm in a Petri dish, where fertilization occurs.

Fertilized eggs at the 1-cell stage are inserted into the Fallopian tube.

GAMETE INTRA-FALLOPIAN TUBE TRANSFER (GIFT)

Eggs are immediately mixed with sperm.

The mixture of sperm and eggs is immediately inserted into the Fallopian tube, where fertilization occurs.

What Is LIFE? SECOND EDITION

A GUIDE TO BIOLOGY

Jay Phelan

25·1–25·3 How do animals reproduce?

Organisms can reproduce sexually or asexually—or both.

SEXUAL vs. ASEXUAL REPRODUCTION

The advantages and disadvantages of sexual and asexual reproduction:

SEXUAL REPRODUCTION

ADVANTAGES
• Offspring are genetically different from each other and from either parent—an evolutionary adaptation that can lead to increased fitness in changing environments.

DISADVANTAGES
• Finding a partner and mating can be difficult and time-consuming.
• Only half of an individual's alleles will be passed to its offspring.

ASEXUAL REPRODUCTION

ADVANTAGES
• Reproduction is fast and efficient.
• All of an individual's alleles are passed on to its offspring.

DISADVANTAGES
• With a changing environment, individuals producing genetically identical offspring are less likely to have offspring suited to the environment.

EXTERNAL vs. INTERNAL FERTILIZATION

Sexual reproduction requires fertilization, which occurs externally in most fishes and amphibians, and internally in most other vertebrates, including humans.

EXTERNAL FERTILIZATION
The sperm and egg unite outside the male's and the female's body.

INTERNAL FERTILIZATION
Sperm are deposited inside the female's reproductive tract and unite with eggs.

25·4–25·7 Male and female reproductive systems have important similarities and differences.

Genetically, the production of eggs barely differs from sperm production, but fewer eggs than sperm are produced, and eggs are much larger than sperm.

MALE REPRODUCTIVE STRUCTURES

The structures of the male reproductive system.

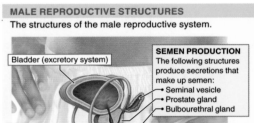

Bladder (excretory system)

Penis

Urethra

Scrotum

Testes

SEMEN PRODUCTION
The following structures produce secretions that make up semen:
• Seminal vesicle
• Prostate gland
• Bulbourethral gland

SPERM PRODUCTION
The following structures play a role in the production and transport of sperm:
• Vas deferens
• Epididymis
• Seminiferous tubules

SPERM PRODUCTION

In adult men, sperm are continuously produced in the testes by meiosis.

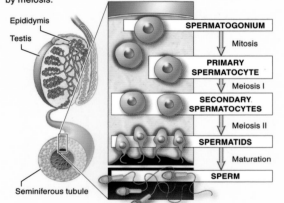

Epididymis

Testis

Seminiferous tubule

SPERMATOGONIUM
↓ Mitosis

PRIMARY SPERMATOCYTE
↓ Meiosis I

SECONDARY SPERMATOCYTES
↓ Meiosis II

SPERMATIDS
↓ Maturation

SPERM

STRUCTURE OF SPERM

The structure of sperm reflects its function.

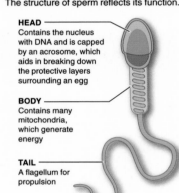

HEAD
Contains the nucleus with DNA and is capped by an acrosome, which aids in breaking down the protective layers surrounding an egg

BODY
Contains many mitochondria, which generate energy

TAIL
A flagellum for propulsion

FEMALE REPRODUCTIVE STRUCTURES

The structures of the female reproductive system.

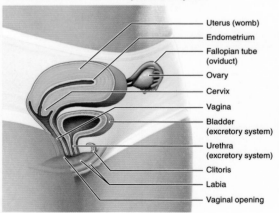

Uterus (womb)

Endometrium

Fallopian tube (oviduct)

Ovary

Cervix

Vagina

Bladder (excretory system)

Urethra (excretory system)

Clitoris

Labia

Vaginal opening

EGG DEVELOPMENT

In adult women, diploid cells in the ovaries undergo meiosis to produce genetically varied haploid eggs.

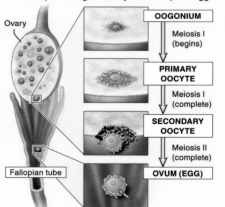

Ovary

Fallopian tube

OOGONIUM
↓ Meiosis I (begins)

PRIMARY OOCYTE
↓ Meiosis I (complete)

SECONDARY OOCYTE
↓ Meiosis II (complete)

OVUM (EGG)

THE FEMALE REPRODUCTIVE CYCLE

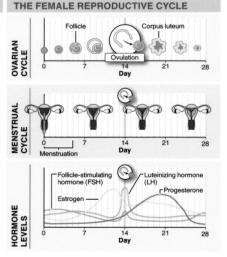

OVARIAN CYCLE
Follicle   Corpus luteum
Ovulation
Day   0   7   14   21   28

MENSTRUAL CYCLE
Menstruation
Day   0   7   14   21   28

HORMONE LEVELS
Follicle-stimulating hormone (FSH)
Luteinizing hormone (LH)
Estrogen
Progesterone
Day   0   7   14   21   28

What Is LIFE? SECOND EDITION
A GUIDE TO BIOLOGY
Jay Phelan

26·1–26·4 Your body has different ways to protect you against disease-causing invaders.

The immune system protects us from a diverse group of pathogens—disease-causing viruses and microorganisms, often referred to as "germs."

DIVISIONS OF THE IMMUNE SYSTEM

The immune system has three basic parts: physical barriers, non-specific immunity, and specific immunity.

PHYSICAL BARRIERS
- Form a nearly impenetrable wall, keeping pathogens from entering body tissues
- Consist of skin, mucous membranes, and their associated anti-pathogen secretions

NON-SPECIFIC IMMUNITY
- Recognizes and destroys pathogens that breach external barriers
- Responds to all pathogens in the same way
- Responds to infection within minutes

SPECIFIC IMMUNITY
- Destroys pathogens that are not killed by non-specific defenses
- Recognizes specific pathogens and forms a memory of each
- Responds to infection in hours to days

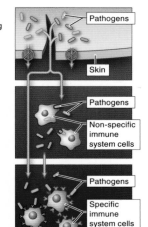

Pathogens / Skin
Pathogens / Non-specific immune system cells
Pathogens / Specific immune system cells

DEFENSE MECHANISMS OF THE INTEGUMENTARY SYSTEM

Physical barriers, part of the integumentary system, prevent pathogens from entering the body's cells; cells exposed to the external environment are protected by defenses such as bacteria-destroying chemicals, acidic secretions, sticky mucus, and wax.

SKIN
This forms a nearly impenetrable barrier that keeps pathogens from entering the body.

CILIA
Hair-like extensions on the surface of the respiratory tract move mucus-entrapped pathogens up and out of the lungs.

LYSOZYME AND OTHER ENZYMES
Lysozyme in saliva and tears, and digestive enzymes in the small intestine, kill many bacteria.

TEARS
Fluid containing antiviral and antibacterial chemicals washes away microorganisms from around the eyes.

ACIDIC SECRETIONS
Stomach acids, acidic vaginal secretions, and acidic urine, all protect the digestive, reproductive, and urinary tracts from bacterial pathogens.

EAR WAX
This sticky substance can trap microorganisms in the ear canal.

THE WHITE BLOOD CELLS OF NON-SPECIFIC IMMUNITY

The non-specific immune system consists of several types of white blood cells that are made in the bone marrow and released into the bloodstream.

NEUTROPHILS
- Phagocytic cells that ingest small organisms, primarily bacteria
- Destroy both the pathogen and themselves in the process
- Nucleus is multi-lobed

DENDRITIC CELLS
- Phagocytic cells (named for their tentacle-like arms, called dendrites) that present ingested pathogens to cells of the specific immune system

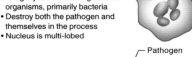

— Pathogen

MACROPHAGES
- Phagocytic cells that ingest whole pathogens as well as large debris such as dead cells
- Present pieces of pathogens on their surface, advertising the infection to cells of the specific immune system

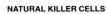

NATURAL KILLER CELLS
- Kill body cells infected by pathogens by poking holes in the cell membranes
- Also play a role in recognizing and killing cancer cells

Infected cell

INFLAMMATION

Inflammation is a major way in which pathogens are eliminated by the non-specific immunity system. The four recognizable signs of the inflammatory response (redness, heat, swelling, and pain) are related to the changes in blood vessels that enhance the recruitment of phagocytes and complement proteins to the site of inflammation.

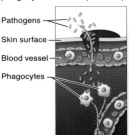

Pathogens
Skin surface
Blood vessel
Phagocytes

26·5–26·9 Specific immunity develops after exposure to pathogens.

(continued on other side) ▶

The memory of the specific division of the immune system can confer immunity, a state of long-term protection against a specific pathogen.

IMMUNITY

Long-term protection, or immunity, from a specific pathogen can form by exposure to the natural pathogen or exposure to a vaccine with an altered version of the pathogen, both of which result in production of antibodies.

ANTIGENS AND ANTIBODIES

ANTIGENS
Foreign substances that induce a specific immune response

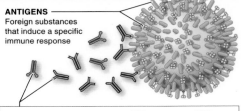

ANTIBODIES
Proteins that recognize certain antigens, enhancing the non-specific system's ability to recognize and destroy those antigens

ANTIBODY FUNCTIONS

Antibodies function in several ways to help destroy pathogens and free-floating antigens.

PHAGOCYTE SIGNALING
Antibodies bind to antigens on the surface of pathogens, making it easier for phagocytes to find the pathogens and destroy them.

PREVENTION OF CELL ENTRY
Antibodies coating the surface of pathogens prevent the pathogens from entering body cells.

ANTIGEN CLUMPING
Antibodies make pathogens and free-floating antigens clump together, making it easier for phagocytes to find them and destroy them.

COMPLEMENT PROTEIN SIGNALING
Antibodies recruit complement proteins, which poke holes in pathogen membranes, causing the pathogen cells to burst.

What Is LIFE? SECOND EDITION — A GUIDE TO BIOLOGY — Jay Phelan

The memory of the specific division of the immune system can confer immunity, a state of long-term protection against a specific pathogen.

THE WHITE BLOOD CELLS OF SPECIFIC IMMUNITY

B cells and T cells are responsible for the specific immunity response. They are named for the location in the body where they mature (the bone marrow and thymus).

B CELLS
• Develop and mature in bone marrow
• Lymphocytes that combat pathogens by releasing antibodies into body fluids when antigens are detected

Antigen receptors

T CELLS
• Develop in bone marrow and mature in the thymus
• Lymphocytes that combat pathogens by directly destroying the infected cells

THE PRIMARY RESPONSE TO INFECTION

The primary response leads to destruction of an antigen and generation of memory cells to fight the antigen should it ever be encountered again.

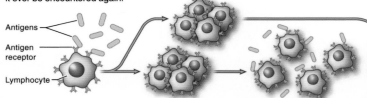

Antigens
Antigen receptor
Lymphocyte

❶ RECOGNITION
When a lymphocyte comes into contact with the antigen specific to its receptor, the cell initiates a response that leads to the destruction of the antigen.

❷ CLONAL SELECTION PRODUCES MEMORY CELLS AND EFFECTOR CELLS
The lymphocyte divides numerous times, creating two populations of cells with the same antigen specificity.

❸ EFFECTOR CELLS ATTACK
Effector cells immediately take action, leading to the destruction of the antigen.

❹ MEMORY CELLS REMEMBER
Memory cells remember the antigen so that if the body is infected with the same antigen in the future, they will be ready to respond.

T CELL-MEDITATED RESPONSE

Antibodies, produced by B cells, cannot destroy pathogens that are inside cells. The specialization of cytotoxic T cells is required to kill infected cells.

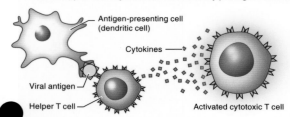

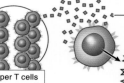
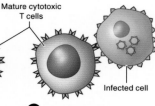

Antigen-presenting cell (dendritic cell)
Cytokines
Viral antigen
Helper T cell
Activated cytotoxic T cell

Cytotoxic T cells (memory and effector cells)
Helper T cells (memory and effector cells)

Cytokines
Mature cytotoxic T cells
Infected cell

❶ PRESENTATION AND RECOGNITION
An antigen-presenting cell displays digested particles of a virus to a helper T cell that recognizes the viral antigen being presented.

❷ ACTIVATION
Binding to the antigen-presenting cell causes the helper T cell to produce cytokines, activating cytotoxic T cells (as well as the B cells of the humoral response).

❸ CLONAL EXPANSION
Both helper T cells and cytotoxic T cells undergo clonal expansion, producing vast amounts of memory and effector cells with specificity for the viral antigen.

❹ MATURATION
Other cytokines produced by the helper T cells make the cytotoxic T cells mature and ready to fight the pathogen.

❺ DESTRUCTION
Mature cytotoxic T cells circulate throughout the body, destroying cells infected with the specific viral antigen.

26·10–26·12 Malfunction of the immune system causes disease.

Genetic defects, environmental influences, and even viruses can trigger immune dysfunction.

AUTOIMMUNITY

When lymphocytes bear receptors that inappropriately recognize structures of a person's own body as foreign invaders, autoimmunity develops. Autoimmune responses can do significant damage to specific organs or to tissues throughout the body, depending on where the antigens are located. For example, type 1 diabetes is an autoimmune disorder in which cytotoxic T cells destroy one's own pancreatic cells.

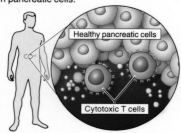

Healthy pancreatic cells
Cytotoxic T cells

IMMUNE SYSTEM DEFICIENCY: HIV

AIDS is an immune system disease caused by the human immunodeficiency virus (HIV). The virus infects helper T cells— immune cells that are crucial to survival. As helper T cells are killed by the infection or by the body's own immune cells in response to the infection, the deficiency of helper T cells leads to complete failure of the specific immunity response. Illness and death occur from infections that a healthy immune system could defeat. There is currently no vaccine for HIV, because traditional vaccine methods do not work against this rapidly mutating virus, nor is there a cure for AIDS.

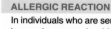

HIV viruses
Lymphocyte

ALLERGIC REACTION

In individuals who are sensitive, an allergen induces a humoral response in which one class of antibodies binds to and activates mast cells. A second exposure to the allergen leads activated mast cells to release histamine and other chemicals, resulting in allergy-related symptoms. Swelling and inflammation can be localized or can be systemic and lead to anaphylactic shock.

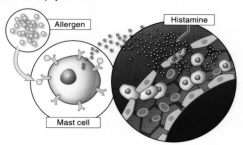

Allergen
Histamine
Mast cell

24·6 – 24·10 Hormones influence nearly every facet of an organism.

Hormones affect a person's physique and physical performance, behavior, mood, and cognitive abilities, as well as health and longevity.

HORMONES CAN AFFECT PHYSIQUE AND PHYSICAL PERFORMANCE

Hormones affect a person's physique and physical performance by influencing gene expression and protein synthesis in cells with testosterone receptors. For example, testosterone has the following affects on the body:

Increase in lean muscle mass

Improved speed and stamina

Reduced production of fat-storage cells

Development of secondary sex characteristics

HORMONES CAN AFFECT MOOD

Many hormones, including estrogen, testosterone, melatonin, and cortisol, have pronounced effects on moods. For example, drastic changes in estrogen levels can cause "the baby blues" in some women shortly after giving birth and testosterone levels surge in victorious competitors, as well as in their fans.

HORMONES CAN AFFECT COGNITIVE PERFORMANCE

A great number of experimental studies demonstrate that cognitive abilities in humans are influenced by hormones, particularly the reproductive hormones estrogen and testosterone, but also the stress hormone cortisol. For example, men and women have slightly different abilities in certain areas, based on the abundance or lack of the hormones testosterone and estrogen.

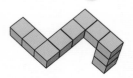

"A box of mixed biscuits in a biscuit mixer."

MOTOR AND VERBAL TASKS
- Females tend to perform better than males on tests of articulation speed and fine-muscle movement.
- The disparity between male and female performance is greatest at points of high estrogen levels in the female reproductive cycle and least at the points of lowest estrogen levels.

SPATIAL TASKS
- Males tend to perform better than females on tests of spatial ability, such as mental rotations of two- or three-dimensional objects.
- Evidence suggests that this performance difference reflects effects of testosterone—although the mechanisms are unclear.

HORMONES CAN AFFECT HEALTH AND LONGEVITY

Hormones affect health and longevity in complex ways. Sterilization of animals, for example, reduces levels of circulating reproductive hormones and increases longevity, usually due to reduced cancer mortality. But in other cases, such as hormone replacement therapy in women, the relationship appears to be reversed, with treatment reducing the annual risk of death by about 25%.

24·11 Environmental contaminants can disrupt normal hormone functioning.

Chemicals in the environment can mimic or block hormones, with disastrous results.

ENDOCRINE DISRUPTORS

Endocrine disruptors are chemicals used by humans that, when taken up by organisms, can mimic, block, or otherwise interfere with hormones and can lead to a variety of adverse physiological effects. Endocrine disruptors are found in thousands of consumer products and detected in numerous natural habitats, as a result of industrial manufacturing processes.

THE ADVERSE EFFECTS OF ENDOCRINE DISRUPTORS

A variety of animal groups appear to have been adversely affected by endocrine disruptors.

MAMMALS
In populations of Baltic ringed seals, endocrine disruptors have interfered with female reproductive functioning, leading to partial or complete sterility in 70% of the animals.

FISHES
In a variety of fish species, including carp, rainbow trout, and flounder, exposure to endocrine disruptors in sewage runoff has been shown to interfere with reproductive functioning.

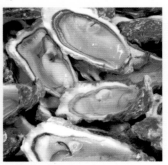

INVERTEBRATES
In marine invertebrates, endocrine disruptors have led to the production of defective shells, as well as the masculinization of female genitals, reducing fertility.

What Is LIFE? A GUIDE TO BIOLOGY **Jay Phelan**

24·1–24·3 Hormones are chemical messengers regulating cell functioning.

The endocrine system consists of all the hormone-secreting cells—including larger collections of cells called endocrine glands—in an animal.

HORMONE SECRETION

Hormones are chemical messengers, secreted by endocrine cells and endocrine glands into the circulatory system, that influence the actions of target cells elsewhere in the body.

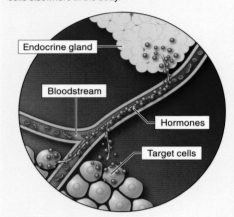

HORMONE TYPES

Most hormones are one of two types, and differences in their chemical structures influence the method by which they regulate activity in a cell.

PEPTIDE AND PROTEIN HORMONES

1 Peptide and protein hormones are water-soluble and therefore cannot pass through cell membranes.

2 The hormones bind to receptors embedded within the cell membrane.

3 Once a hormone binds to a receptor, its alteration of the receptor causes any one of a number of changes within the cell.

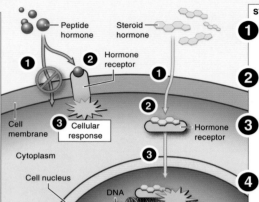

STEROID HORMONES

1 Steroid hormones are lipid-soluble and therefore can pass through cell membranes.

2 The hormones then bind to receptors located within the cytoplasm or nucleus of the cell.

3 If not already in the nucleus, the hormone-receptor complex will generally pass into the nucleus.

4 Once in the nucleus, the hormone-receptor complex may bind to DNA, influencing gene expression.

24·4–24·5 Hormones are produced in glands throughout the body.

Endocrine glands throughout the body are responsible for detecting and responding to signals that reflect an organism's internal and external environments.

THE ENDOCRINE GLANDS

Functions of the glands of the endocrine system:

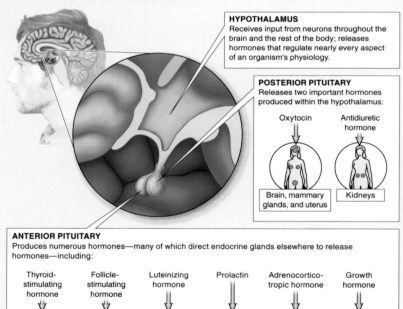

HYPOTHALAMUS
Receives input from neurons throughout the brain and the rest of the body; releases hormones that regulate nearly every aspect of an organism's physiology.

POSTERIOR PITUITARY
Releases two important hormones produced within the hypothalamus:

Oxytocin — Brain, mammary glands, and uterus
Antidiuretic hormone — Kidneys

ANTERIOR PITUITARY
Produces numerous hormones—many of which direct endocrine glands elsewhere to release hormones—including:

Thyroid-stimulating hormone — Thyroid
Follicle-stimulating hormone — Ovaries and testes
Luteinizing hormone — Ovaries and testes
Prolactin — Mammary glands
Adrenocorticotropic hormone — Adrenal glands
Growth hormone — Liver and many other organs

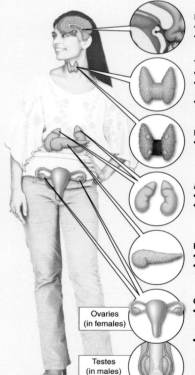

PINEAL GLAND
• Releases melatonin
• Regulates sleep cycles

THYROID GLAND
• Releases thyroxine
• Influences the rate and efficiency of cellular metabolism
• Regulates calcium levels in the blood

PARATHYROID GLANDS
• Regulate calcium levels in the blood

ADRENAL GLANDS
• Release adrenaline and cortisol
• Regulate organism's response to stress

PANCREAS
• Releases insulin and glucagon
• Maintains blood glucose levels within a narrow range

GONADS
• Release the sex steroids, including testosterone, estrogen, and progesterone
• Responsible for numerous physical, behavioral, and emotional features, including much sexual behavior, development, and growth

Ovaries (in females)
Testes (in males)

What Is LIFE? SECOND EDITION — A GUIDE TO BIOLOGY — **Jay Phelan**

23·15–23·16 The muscular and skeletal systems enable movement.

Muscle tissue—including skeletal, cardiac, and smooth muscle—is made up of elongated cells capable of generating force when they contract.

SKELETAL MUSCLE

Skeletal muscle is responsible for generating most of the movement we see in vertebrates.

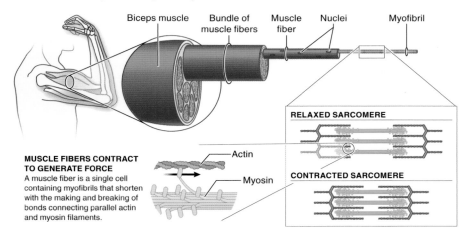

Biceps muscle Bundle of muscle fibers Muscle fiber Nuclei Myofibril

RELAXED SARCOMERE

Actin

CONTRACTED SARCOMERE

Myosin

MUSCLE FIBERS CONTRACT TO GENERATE FORCE
A muscle fiber is a single cell containing myofibrils that shorten with the making and breaking of bonds connecting parallel actin and myosin filaments.

FUNCTIONS OF THE SKELETAL SYSTEM

STRUCTURAL SUPPORT
Provides shape and structure, including securing organs in place

PROTECTION
Shields vulnerable tissue—such as the brain and heart—from external insults

ENABLING MOVEMENT
Muscles, which are connected to bones, generate movement when they contract

CELL PRODUCTION
Produces blood cells in bone marrow

MINERAL RESERVOIR
Elements such as calcium can be released from or stored in bones in response to deficiencies or excesses in the bloodstream

23·17–23·18 The brain is organized into distinct structures dedicated to specific functions.

There are several distinct regions in the brain each of which is the control center for various activities in the body.

PRINCIPAL REGIONS OF THE BRAIN

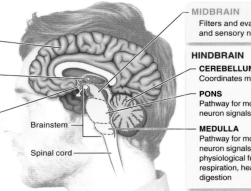

FOREBRAIN

CEREBRAL CORTEX
Involved in abstract thought, problem solving, and language

THALAMUS
Receives sensory input and relays some signals to the cerebral cortex while blocking others

HYPOTHALAMUS
Regulates many fundamental drives, including hunger and thirst, sexual activity, and maintenance of body temperature; controls the hormone secretions of the tiny pituitary gland

Brainstem

Spinal cord

MIDBRAIN
Filters and evaluates motor and sensory neuron signals

HINDBRAIN

CEREBELLUM
Coordinates motor activity

PONS
Pathway for motor and sensory neuron signals

MEDULLA
Pathway for motor and sensory neuron signals; regulates basic physiological functions such as respiration, heart rate, and digestion

REGIONS OF THE CEREBRAL CORTEX

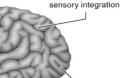

FRONTAL LOBE
Regulates speech production, motor control, smell, problem solving, and many aspects of personality

PARIETAL LOBE
Receives and perceives touch and pressure sensations; important in sensory integration

TEMPORAL LOBE
Perceives and processes auditory and visual sensations; important in pattern recognition and language comprehension

OCCIPITAL LOBE
Receives and processes visual information

23·19–23·21 Drugs can hijack pleasure pathways.

Drugs can have various effects, some of which are used in the treatment of diseases and some of which are used to create sought-after euphoric or excited states.

TRICKED BY CHEMICALS

Our brain's signaling system can be tricked by drugs, whether recreational or therapeutic, that mimic neurotransmitters. Such drugs—including cocaine, Prozac, heroin, and nicotine—can produce euphoric

sensations, can reduce depression, and can block pain, but the effects often come with significant health risks.

CAFFEINE

Normal neural activity leads to a buildup of cellular waste products. One of these, adenosine, fills adenosine receptors on nearby neurons, reducing the likelihood that a neuron will initiate an action potential and causing fatigue. Caffeine binds to adenosine receptors,

but without reducing their likelihood of firing, thus blocking the fatigue-inducing message of adenosine.

ALCOHOL

Alcohol affects the functioning of multiple neurotransmitters—including glutamate, endorphins, dopamine, and serotonin—slowing reaction times, slurring speech, blocking pain, and increasing contentment.

 What Is LIFE? A GUIDE TO BIOLOGY Jay Phelan SECOND EDITION

23 NERVOUS and MOTOR SYSTEMS...*to go*

23·1– 23·3 What is the nervous system?

Nervous systems are found in all multicellular animals other than sponges.

FUNCTIONS OF THE NERVOUS SYSTEM

The nervous system has three primary functions.

RECEIVE STIMULI
The nervous system collects information about the internal and external environments.

PROCESS INFORMATION
The nervous system interprets the incoming stimuli and determines a response.

INITIATE RESPONSE
The nervous system sends signals to muscles and glands in response to the internal and external environments.

NEURON STRUCTURE

Neurons—individual cells that specialize in carrying electrical signals—are the building blocks of the nervous system.

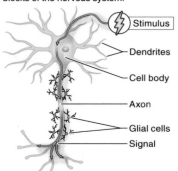

- Stimulus
- Dendrites
- Cell body
- Axon
- Glial cells
- Signal

THE VERTEBRATE NERVOUS SYSTEM

In vertebrates, the nervous system is divided into the central nervous system and the peripheral nervous system.

CENTRAL NERVOUS SYSTEM

The central nervous system—made up of the spinal cord and brain—processes information from sensory cells and sends out instructions to other nervous tissue to act in response to that sensory information.

PERIPHERAL NERVOUS SYSTEM

The peripheral nervous system carries signals to and from the sensory and motor pathways. The motor pathways carry signals from both the somatic and the autonomic nervous systems, which relay signals that can be controlled consciously, as well as other signals that cannot be controlled consciously.

23·4– 23·7 How do neurons work?

Neurons are cells specialized for receiving information via their dendrites and transmitting this information through action potentials down their axons.

DENDRITES

Receptor proteins within the cell membrane of the dendrite respond to stimuli by briefly opening up little channels.

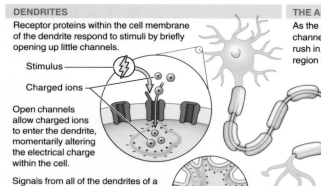

- Stimulus
- Charged ions

Open channels allow charged ions to enter the dendrite, momentarily altering the electrical charge within the cell.

Signals from all of the dendrites of a neuron converge. If the sum total of signals coming in is significantly positive, then the cell initiates an action potential that travels down the axon.

- Action potential

THE AXON

As the action potential moves down an axon, ion channels allow positively charged sodium ions to rush in, changing the cell's charge to positive in that region and thus propagating the action potential.

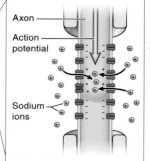

- Axon
- Action potential
- Sodium ions

THE SYNAPSE

At the synapse, a neuron interacts with other cells. In response to an action potential, neurotransmitters are released into the synaptic cleft, diffuse, and may bind to receptors on an adjacent neuron, muscle cell, or gland, potentially stimulating an action potential, muscle contraction, or secretion.

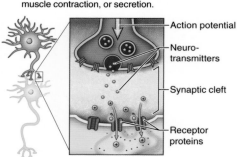

- Action potential
- Neuro-transmitters
- Synaptic cleft
- Receptor proteins

23·8– 23·14 Our senses detect and transmit stimuli.

The process by which all our senses work is basically the same. A modified dendrite on a sensory neuron is stimulated by some aspect of the outside world.

TASTE

Your tongue has about 10,000 taste buds, each of which contains 60–80 chemoreceptors, which are stimulated when particular chemicals in food bind to receptor proteins on the cell surface. The binding of chemicals to these receptors triggers an action potential that delivers a taste sensation to the brain.

SMELL

Neurons that can detect smells have dendrites modified with tiny, hair-like projections covered with chemoreceptors. Airborne chemicals move through mucus in the nasal cavity and bind to the smell receptors, triggering action potentials that travel into the smell center of the brain, where the signal is perceived as a particular odor.

VISION

Vision results from the stimulation of light-sensitive sensory neurons, called photoreceptor cells. Signals are conveyed to the brain and interpreted as an image. The particular wavelength perceived depends on which version of the light-sensitive molecules in the photoreceptor cell membranes is stimulated.

HEARING

Hearing occurs when sound waves cause the eardrum to vibrate, moving tiny bones that pass on the vibrations to the inner ear, where they bend hair cells and thus trigger a pattern of action potentials that varies according to the wavelengths of the sound. This is interpreted by the brain as sound.

TOUCH

Touch is a class of sensations generated by mechano-receptors, thermoreceptors, and pain receptors located throughout the body. Stimulation of these receptors causes a change in the shape of the sensory neuron's membrane, altering its permeability, generating action potentials, and causing the perception of touch by the brain.

What Is LIFE? SECOND EDITION A GUIDE TO BIOLOGY Jay Phelan

22·8 – 22·13 We extract energy and nutrients from food.

The digestive process in humans includes four distinct phases: ingestion, digestion, absorption, and elimination.

INGESTION

Ingestion is the first phase of the digestive process. Usually lasting less than a minute, ingestion involves tearing and grinding food in preparation for passing it to the stomach. Digestion also begins during this phase, with some starch being broken down by enzymes in saliva.

DIGESTION

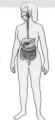

Digestion—the process of dismantling large pieces of food, physically and chemically breaking them down into absorbable molecules—is the second phase of the breakdown of food in animals. It occurs primarily in the stomach and small intestine.

ABSORPTION

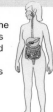

Absorption is the process by which energy-rich food particles are taken up from the digestive tract into the cells of the body, where they can be used for energy and building materials. Absorption takes place primarily in the small intestine.

ELIMINATION

The last phase of food breakdown takes place as the mostly indigestible materials leave the small intestine and enter the large intestine, or colon. There, water and ions are absorbed before the remaining materials are defecated.

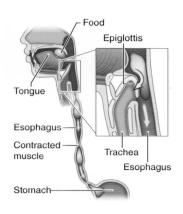

Food — Epiglottis — Tongue — Esophagus — Contracted muscle — Trachea — Esophagus — Stomach

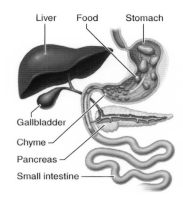

Liver — Food — Stomach — Gallbladder — Chyme — Pancreas — Small intestine

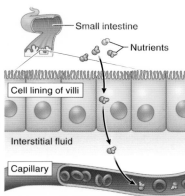

Small intestine — Nutrients — Cell lining of villi — Interstitial fluid — Capillary

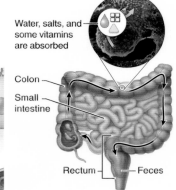

Water, salts, and some vitamins are absorbed — Colon — Small intestine — Rectum — Feces

22·14 – 22·18 What we eat profoundly affects our health.

At the most basic level, just two requirements—quality and quantity—must be satisfied in the design of a healthy diet.

RECOMMENDED DAILY FOOD INTAKE

A balanced diet contains adequate amounts of essential nutrients and energy, but not surplus amounts, and is low in substances—including saturated fats, cholesterol, sugar, salt, and alcohol—that can have adverse health effects when consumed in greater quantities. Because no one food is completely adequate, nutritionists recommend consuming a variety of foods from each of the basic food groups.

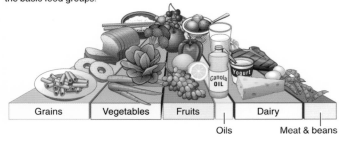

Grains | Vegetables | Fruits | Dairy | Oils | Meat & beans

DIABETES: TYPE 1 vs. TYPE 2

Digesting and absorbing food leads to an increase in the amount of glucose circulating in the bloodstream, which triggers the release of insulin by the pancreas, causing the body's cells, especially muscle cells and fat cells, to pull the glucose in for energy or storage. Problems with regulation of blood sugar, called diabetes, affect millions of people and are caused by heredity and poor diet.

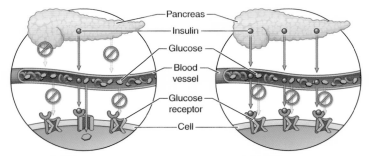

Pancreas — Insulin — Glucose — Blood vessel — Glucose receptor — Cell

TYPE 1 DIABETES
The pancreas doesn't secrete enough insulin in response to an increase in blood sugar.

TYPE 2 DIABETES
The pancreas secretes plenty of insulin, but the cells of the body don't respond to it, usually due to a deficiency in glucose receptors on the cell membranes.

WEIGHT LOSS

Weight loss is both a simple and a complicated problem. There is only one complete and perfect plan that guarantees success: reduced caloric intake and increased caloric expenditure. Interventions designed to facilitate weight loss involve drugs, surgery, or behavior modification, none of which is reliably successful and safe.

SPICE USE AND ANTIMICROBIAL PROPERTIES

Somewhat ironically, humans may seek out toxic compounds that are produced by plants to ward off predators. Such compounds, used as spices, may help us fight off illness-inducing microorganisms.

22·1–22·3 Food provides the raw materials for growth and the fuel to make it happen.

Animals must eat for two reasons: to acquire the energy needed for all growth and activity, and to acquire the raw materials required for life.

MADE POSSIBLE BY FOOD

Living organisms need raw materials and fuel to function.

FOOD

DIGESTION
Food is physically and chemically broken down.

NUTRIENTS
Substances that are used for energy, raw materials, and maintenance of the body's systems

WASTE
Unneeded or unusable material that is eliminated after passing through the digestive system

TYPES OF ANIMAL DIETS

In the animal world, species fall into three groups based on their diets.

  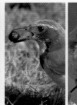

CARNIVORES
Animals that consume only other animals.

HERBIVORES
Animals that consume only plants.

OMNIVORES
Animals that consume both plants and animals.

COMPONENTS OF ENERGY EXPENDITURE

To function well, living organisms need sufficient energy, measured in kilocalories. The minimal energy needed by an individual not engaged in any activity is called its basal metabolic rate, or BMR.

BASAL METABOLIC RATE (BMR)
The minimal energy expenditure of an organism at rest

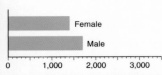

Average kcal/day to cover the minimal energetic needs of an organism at rest

ACTUAL DAILY ENERGY EXPENDITURE
The basal metabolic rate *plus* the energy required for all activity (individuals generally need about 50% to 100% more kilocalories per day than their BMR)

 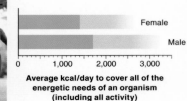

Average kcal/day to cover all of the energetic needs of an organism (including all activity)

22·4–22·7 Nutrients are grouped into six categories.

These six groups of nutrients are the substances that are used for energy, raw materials, and maintenance of the body's systems.

WATER

Water is probably the single most important component of an animal's diet. It constitutes 60% to 65% of the body weight of most mammals. It transports nutrients and waste materials throughout the body, takes part in metabolic reactions, serves as a solvent, lubricates many body parts, and helps regulate body temperature.

VITAMINS AND MINERALS

Vitamins and minerals are, respectively, organic and inorganic molecules in the diet. They are used in the production and action of enzymes and other molecules involved in the processing of food and other biochemical reactions. While vitamins and minerals are essential in small amounts, most people in the United States meet their needs from food and do not benefit from taking them as supplements.

PROTEIN

FUNCTION
Once proteins in foods are broken down, the amino acids are used as the raw materials to build new complex proteins, such as hemoglobin and muscle.

SOURCE
• Animals: egg whites, shrimp, tuna, poultry, and meat
• Plants: grains, vegetables, nuts, seeds, and legumes

STORAGE
• Amino acids are usually stored for less than half a day before being reassembled into proteins throughout the body
• Can be converted to fat and stored in fat cells

CARBOHYDRATES

FUNCTION
Carbohydrates provide energy to fuel movement, growth, and all cellular activities in the body.

SOURCE
• Fruits, vegetables, and grains

STORAGE
• Carbohydrates are stored in the liver and muscle cells as glycogen for about a day before being broken down to provide energy
• Can be converted to fat and stored in fat cells

FATS

FUNCTION
Fats provide a dense source of energy that can be efficiently stored in the body, and they aid in keeping the body warm.

SOURCE
• Butter, cheese, oils, eggs, and meat

STORAGE
• Fats are stored in fat cells throughout the body

21·4 – 21·10 The human circulatory system consists of a heart, blood vessels, and blood. ◀ (continued from other side)

Blood flows from the heart to the tissues of the body and back to the heart again through a series of endothelium-lined blood vessels.

LDL vs. HDL CHOLESTEROL

Cholesterol can be helpful or harmful.

HIGH-DENSITY LIPOPROTEIN (HDL)
• "Good" cholesterol
• Tends to remove cholesterol from arteries and deliver it to liver cells, where it can be broken down

LOW-DENSITY LIPOPROTEIN (LDL)
• "Bad" cholesterol
• Tends to adhere to artery walls, where it can initiate the buildup of dangerous plaques

THE HUMAN LYMPHATIC SYSTEM

The lymphatic system runs close to the circulatory system throughout the body and plays a supporting role in the process of circulation.

Lymph node

Lymphatic capillary

FUNCTIONS OF THE LYMPHATIC SYSTEM

The lymphatic system supports the circulatory system while fighting illness.

RECYCLING
The lymphatic system recycles fluid and proteins that diffuse from the blood capillaries during circulation back into the bloodstream.

FIGHTING ILLNESS
As lymph circulates through the body, white-blood-cell-packed lymph nodes remove dangerous materials, including bacteria, cancer cells, and viruses.

RETRIEVING NUTRIENTS
Little projections that extend into the small intestine absorb lipids from the digestive tract and shuttle them to the bloodstream.

21·11 – 21·16 The respiratory system enables gas exchange in animals.

Aerobic respiration requires cells to take up oxygen and release carbon dioxide.

GAS EXCHANGE IN ANIMALS

In large, multicellular organisms, gas exchange is a two-stage process.

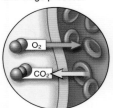
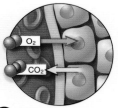

1 Respiratory gases are exchanged between the external environment and the circulatory system.

2 Respiratory gases are exchanged between the circulatory system and the cells involved in cellular respiration.

HEMOGLOBIN

Red blood cells are filled with hemoglobin, which picks up oxygen in the lungs and transports it around the body, releasing it in organs and tissues for cellular respiration.

THE HUMAN RESPIRATORY SYSTEM

In humans and other terrestrial animals, the respiratory system provides the route for inhaled air to meet the blood vessels of the body.

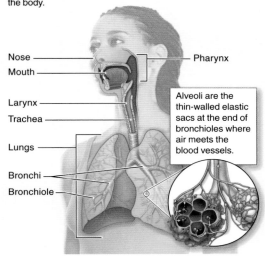

Nose — — Pharynx
Mouth

Larynx
Trachea

Alveoli are the thin-walled elastic sacs at the end of bronchioles where air meets the blood vessels.

Lungs

Bronchi
Bronchiole

THE MECHANICS OF BREATHING

In reptiles, birds, and mammals, breathing occurs in two steps.

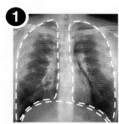

1 **INHALATION**
• Diaphragm and intercostal muscles contract
• Diaphragm is pulled lower and rib cage expands
• Air is sucked into the lungs

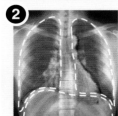

2 **EXHALATION**
• Diaphragm and intercostal muscles relax
• Chest cavity returns to its original size
• Air is forced back out to the trachea

21·17 – 21·18 Evolutionary adaptations maximize oxygen delivery.

Animals living at high elevations have special adaptations to the low-oxygen conditions.

BREATHING AT HIGH ALTITUDES

At high elevations, the amount of oxygen present is lower, and breathing and activity are difficult. Animals living at high elevations solve this problem by producing a form of hemoglobin that has a higher affinity for oxygen.

HUMANS ACCLIMATE TO HIGH ELEVATION LIVING

Humans living at high elevations become acclimated to low-oxygen conditions over the course of three to five weeks. This acclimation includes increasing the production of diphosphoglyceric acid (DPG) in red blood cells and thereby reducing hemoglobin's affinity for oxygen, leading to release of higher levels of oxygen to muscles during exertion.

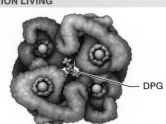

— DPG

DPG-modified hemoglobin

 **What Is LIFE?** SECOND EDITION **A GUIDE TO BIOLOGY** **Jay Phelan**

21 CIRCULATION and RESPIRATION...*to go*

21·1–21·3 The circulatory system is the chief route of distribution in animals.

The circulatory system transports gases, nutrients, waste products, immune system cells, and hormones. It also helps animals maintain homeostasis.

FUNCTIONS OF THE CIRCULATORY SYSTEM

In vertebrates, circulatory systems have three principal functions:

TRANSPORT
Transports oxygen, nutrients, waste products, immune system cells, and hormones in the blood throughout the body.

TEMPERATURE REGULATION
Helps to maintain body temperature within the optimum range for metabolic functioning.

PROTECTION
A variety of cells and chemicals contribute to the individual's defenses against infection by pathogens.

NO CIRCULATORY SYSTEM REQUIRED

Some animals, such as jellyfish and other cnidarians, do not have circulatory systems. Instead, they obtain oxygen and nutrients, and eliminate waste, through diffusion.

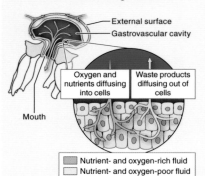

- External surface
- Gastrovascular cavity
- Mouth

Oxygen and nutrients diffusing into cells	Waste products diffusing out of cells

☐ Nutrient- and oxygen-rich fluid
☐ Nutrient- and oxygen-poor fluid

CIRCULATORY SYSTEMS

Circulatory systems can be open or closed.

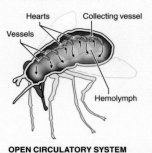

Hearts — Collecting vessel
Vessels
Hemolymph

Vessels — Heart

OPEN CIRCULATORY SYSTEM
- No distinction between circulating fluid and interstitial fluid
- Heart(s) pump the hemolymph throughout the extracellular spaces inside the body
- Insects and most mollusks

CLOSED CIRCULATORY SYSTEM
- Blood is contained within vessels, separated from interstitial fluid
- Muscular heart propels blood through vessels to body tissues
- All vertebrates

TYPES OF BLOOD VESSELS

ARTERIES
Vessels that carry blood away from the heart and to the capillaries.

CAPILLARIES
Tiny porous vessels that bring blood close to tissue, enabling the diffusion of gases, nutrients, and other molecules into and out of the tissue.

VEINS
Vessels that carry blood away from the capillaries back toward the heart.

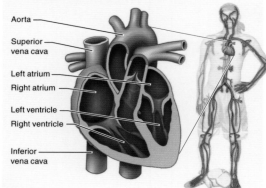

From heart

Diffusion into and out of tissue

To heart

☐ Oxygen-rich blood ☐ Oxygen-poor blood

TYPES OF CLOSED CIRCULATORY SYSTEMS

Vertebrates' circulatory systems vary in structure. Fishes have two-chambered hearts, with one circuit of flow. Birds and mammals have four-chambered hearts and two circuits of flow. This enables blood to be pumped to the body at higher pressure. Amphibians and most reptiles have a three-chambered heart and two circuits of blood flow.

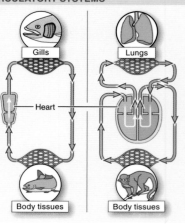

Gills — Lungs — Lungs
Heart
Body tissues — Body tissues — Body tissues

PULMONARY CIRCUIT
Blood is pumped to the lungs, where it picks up oxygen.

SYSTEMIC CIRCUIT
Blood is pumped to the tissues of the body, where it delivers oxygen.

21·4–21·10 The human circulatory system consists of a heart, blood vessels, and blood.

(continued on other side) ▶

Blood flows from the heart to the tissues of the body and back to the heart again through a series of endothelium-lined blood vessels.

THE HUMAN CIRCULATORY SYSTEM

The human circulatory system is composed of a fist-sized heart and an intricate system of blood vessels.

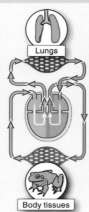

- Aorta
- Superior vena cava
- Left atrium
- Right atrium
- Left ventricle
- Right ventricle
- Inferior vena cava

CONSTITUENTS OF BLOOD

Blood has several distinct components, which we can identify by putting a sample of blood in a test tube and spinning it rapidly in a centrifuge.

PLASMA
- Salty water (generally 90% of plasma)
- Variety of molecules, including metabolites and wastes, salts and ions, and hundreds of plasma proteins

PACKED CELLS
- Red blood cells (generally more than 95% of the packed cells)
- White blood cells
- Platelets (cell fragments)

55%

45%

CARDIOVASCULAR DISEASE

Cardiovascular disease includes all of the diseases of the heart and blood vessels, including heart attacks and strokes.

ATHEROSCLEROSIS
Cholesterol circulating in the bloodstream forms a fatty plaque that reduces the flow of blood.

ARTERIOSCLEROSIS
Calcium is deposited in the plaque, causing it to harden.

HEART ATTACK
A heart attack is caused when there is an interruption in the flow of blood through one of the coronary arteries.

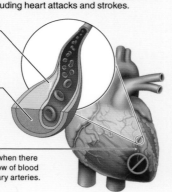

What Is LIFE? SECOND EDITION A GUIDE TO BIOLOGY **Jay Phelan**

20·7–20·8 Animals have an internal environment.

Although the internal environment of multicellular animals is continuously influenced by their external environment, many animals maintain homeostasis.

OUR INTERNAL ENVIRONMENT

Failure to maintain a consistent internal physical and chemical environment can lead to multiple problems in the normal functioning of cells, tissues, and organs, and can result in death.

MAINTAINING HOMEOSTASIS

Organisms maintain a variety of internal physiological variables—including temperature, water-solute balances, pH, blood sugar levels, and blood gas concentrations—within relatively constant ranges. The process of maintaining an organism's internal environment is called homeostasis.

EXTERNAL TEMPERATURE	INTERNAL TEMPERATURE	EXTERNAL TEMPERATURE
110°F	98.6°F	19°F

20·9–20·12 How does homeostasis work?

For animals to maintain homeostasis with regard to a particular physiological variable, that variable must have a set point to which the organism can return.

NEGATIVE FEEDBACK LOOP

In animals, negative feedback systems are the most common method used to maintain the internal environment within a narrow range. In a negative feedback loop, sensors detect change in the internal environment and trigger effectors to oppose or reduce the change.

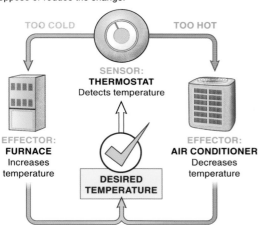

TOO COLD — TOO HOT

SENSOR:
THERMOSTAT
Detects temperature

EFFECTOR:
FURNACE
Increases temperature

EFFECTOR:
AIR CONDITIONER
Decreases temperature

DESIRED TEMPERATURE

GENERATING BODY HEAT

In thermoregulation, the biggest distinction among animal species is in how they generate their body heat.

ENDOTHERMS
• Generate body heat internally
• Sometimes described as "warm-blooded"
• Include most mammals and birds

ECTOTHERMS
• Get their heat primarily from the environment
• Sometimes described as "cold-blooded"
• Include invertebrates, fishes, amphibians, and reptiles

MAINTAINING BODY TEMPERATURE

An animal's ability to maintain body temperature is another important aspect of thermoregulation.

HOMEOTHERMS
Body temperature remains relatively constant.

HETEROTHERMS
Body temperature fluctuates as environmental temperatures change.

OSMOREGULATORY STRATEGIES

Many organisms maintain their water content within a narrow range. To maintain osmotic balance, organisms must be able to take up water and get rid of water, and they must be able to regulate concentrations of ions in their body fluids. Various mechanisms and strategies have evolved for coping with these challenges.

OSMOCONFORMERS

Osmoconformers are organisms that let the composition of their body fluids reflect that of their environment.

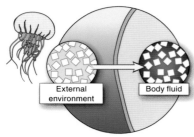

External environment — Body fluid

OSMOREGULATORS

Osmoregulators are organisms that maintain their fluids and solute concentrations within narrow ranges that differ from those of their environment.

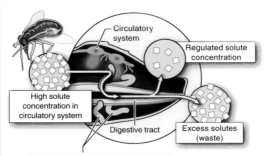

Circulatory system

Regulated solute concentration

High solute concentration in circulatory system

Digestive tract

Excess solutes (waste)

MALPIGHIAN TUBULES (IN INSECTS)
These small tubes regulate osmotic balance in insects by removing excess solutes from the circulatory system.

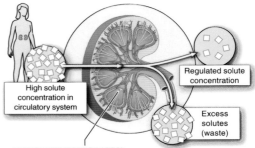

Regulated solute concentration

High solute concentration in circulatory system

Excess solutes (waste)

KIDNEY (IN VERTEBRATES)
This complex organ regulates osmotic balance in vertebrates by removing either excess solutes or excess water from the circulatory system, depending on the organism's external environment.

What Is **LIFE?** SECOND EDITION

A GUIDE TO BIOLOGY

Jay Phelan

20·1–20·6 Animal body structures reflect their functions.

At all levels of animal organization, from molecules to whole organisms, the physical features of a structure are closely related to its function.

FORM FOLLOWS FUNCTION

If a structure is the product of natural selection, the structure commonly reflects closely its function. For example, fast-swimming organisms have streamlined body shapes.

ORGANIZATION OF ANIMAL BODIES

One of the fundamental features of the organization of the animal body is that it is hierarchical, containing four levels of organization.

CELL
The smallest unit of organization in all organisms

TISSUE
Group of cells that share similar structure and function

ORGAN
Group of tissues that perform specialized functions

ORGAN SYSTEM
Group of organs that work together to accomplish one or a few, usually related, physiological functions

TYPES OF ANIMAL TISSUES

Adult animals generally have four main types of tissue.

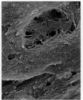 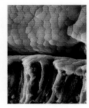  

CONNECTIVE TISSUE
• Composed of cells interspersed throughout a matrix
• Provides structure and support, anchors cells, and regulates communication between cells

EPITHELIAL TISSUE
• Composed of cells that cover and line most surfaces of animal bodies
• Forms the skin and the lining of the lungs, digestive tract, and blood vessels

MUSCLE TISSUE
• Composed of cells that can contract
• Generates movement, pumps fluid, and moves substances

NERVOUS TISSUE
• Composed of specialized cells that send and receive electrical signals
• Stores and transmits information

THE ORGAN SYSTEMS

In nearly all animals, some tissues are organized into organs that serve specialized functions and consist of multiple tissue types, and organs into organ systems that carry out the various physiological processes necessary for growth, development, maintenance, and reproduction.

   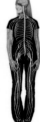

DIGESTIVE SYSTEM
Disassembles and absorbs food so the body can acquire the nutrients it needs to function

CIRCULATORY SYSTEM
Transports gases, nutrients, waste products, hormones, and immune system cells throughout the body

RESPIRATORY SYSTEM
Provides a site for gas exchange between the external environment and an organism's circulatory system

NERVOUS SYSTEM
Acts as the control center of the body and interprets, stores, and transmits information, using electrical impulses and chemical signals

REPRODUCTIVE SYSTEM (MALE)
Produces sperm and delivers them to the female reproductive system, where fertilization may occur

REPRODUCTIVE SYSTEM (FEMALE)
Produces eggs and provides an environment that can nurture a developing embryo and fetus, if fertilization occurs

IMMUNE AND LYMPHATIC SYSTEM
Attacks pathogens that threaten the body and plays a supporting role in circulation by recycling fluid that leaks from the circulatory system

URINARY/EXCRETORY SYSTEM
Purifies the blood by filtering out wastes and transports wastes out of the body

ENDOCRINE SYSTEM
Regulates body activities by releasing hormones that travel through vessels in the circulatory system to reach target cells

INTEGUMENTARY SYSTEM
Provides protection by forming a barrier between the inside and outside of an organism and can aid in the secretion and transport of molecules
—Hair
—Skin
—Nails

SKELETAL SYSTEM
Supports and protects the body and internal organs, manufactures blood cells, and provides a surface for muscle attachment, creating a foundation for movement

MUSCULAR SYSTEM
Generates force through contraction, which enables movement of the body and of blood, food, and other substances throughout the body

What Is LIFE? SECOND EDITION — A GUIDE TO BIOLOGY — **Jay Phelan**

19·7–19·9 External cues trigger internal responses.

Plants have a variety of growth patterns known as tropisms by which they grow toward or away from various environmental stimuli.

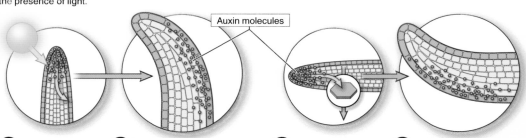

PHOTOTROPISM

Phototropism is plant growth that is influenced by the presence of light.

Auxin molecules

1 Auxins produced in the plant move away from the light source to the shaded side of a stem.

2 Auxins on the shaded side of the stem stimulate a greater rate of growth than on the side with less auxin, causing the plant to bend toward the light.

GRAVITROPISM

Gravitropism is growth in response to gravity.

1 Starches within the cells of the stem sink downward in response to gravity, triggering the movement of auxin toward them.

2 Auxin then stimulates faster growth where it occurs in higher concentration, causing the stem to bend upward.

THIGMOTROPISM

Thigmotropism is growth in response to touch or physical contact.

Climbing plants produce tendrils, which are specialized thread-like leaves or stems that wrap around whatever they touch.

THE BIOLOGICAL CLOCK IN PLANTS

Plants have internal methods of timekeeping—influenced by the external environment—and so can initiate actions at the right time (such as orienting leaves horizontally during the day and vertically at night).

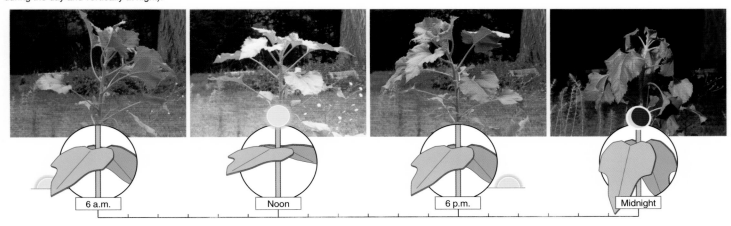

6 a.m. Noon 6 p.m. Midnight

PHOTOPERIODISM

Plants exhibit photoperiodism, responding to seasonal changes over the course of a year and timing their production of flowers or initiation of winter dormancy, for example, according to environmental factors such as the length of darkness each night. All flowering plants fall into one of three categories when it comes to regulating their flower production.

LONG-DAY PLANTS
• Flower production is triggered by decreasing periods of darkness (generally in spring)
• Species include: carnations and clovers

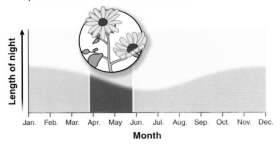

SHORT-DAY PLANTS
• Flower production is triggered by increasing periods of darkness (generally in late summer or fall)
• Species include: poinsettias and strawberries

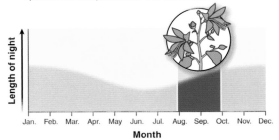

DAY-NEUTRAL PLANTS
• Flower production is triggered by a sufficient state of maturity and not by periods of darkness
• Species include: roses and tomatoes

What Is LIFE? A GUIDE TO BIOLOGY — Jay Phelan

19·1–19·2 Plants defend themselves from herbivores and survive extreme environments.

Plants, rooted in the ground, have a variety of physical and biochemical methods by which they reduce the impact of predation and inhospitable environments.

METHODS OF REDUCING PREDATION

Plants are targets for predators and pathogens. However, they have numerous defenses that can help them reduce the varied and persistent efforts of other organisms to access the valuable resources that they contain.

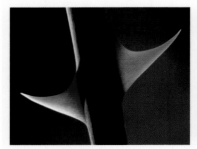

MECHANICAL DEFENSES
Thorns, spines, and hairs can be a deterrent to many herbivores. Additionally, leaves covered with waxy compounds can reduce herbivory, and plants that produce and exude sticky saps or resins can deter or even drown potential insect pests.

CHEMICAL DEFENSES
One of the most common methods that plants use to fight herbivory is the production of chemical compounds that deter herbivores by making the plant toxic or reducing its digestibility.

MIMICRY AND CAMOUFLAGE
One species of passion flower produces leaves with spots that mimic butterfly eggs (above), reducing the likelihood that a butterfly will actually lay eggs on them. On hatching, the insects begin eating the plant, often causing significant damage.

ENLISTING OTHER ORGANISMS FOR "SECURITY"
In acacia plants, ants hollow out thorns and live inside them. In exchange for their "room and board," the ants quickly and aggressively attack any potential leaf-eating insects.

METHODS OF SURVIVING EXTREME ENVIRONMENTS

Evolution has produced plants with adaptations to some of the most extreme of the world's habitats, including super-dry regions, salty environments, and cold, windy habitats.

SUPER-DRY ENVIRONMENTS
In deserts, groundwater is scarce, and moisture loss due to evaporation in the hot temperatures can further constrain a plant's ability to retain water. Plants have responded to these difficult conditions with several different types of adaptations such as thick, fleshy, water-storing tissue in the leaves and stems, strong and deep taproots, and seeds that can remain dormant for long periods of time.

SALTY ENVIRONMENTS
Extreme levels of salt from the ocean and large fluctuations in salt concentrations can make it difficult for cells to maintain a constant water balance and carry out normal metabolic processes. Plants adapted to saltwater environments are able to transport much of the absorbed salt to vacuoles within their cells, thus isolating and containing it where it has little impact on cellular metabolism.

COLD AND WINDY ENVIRONMENTS
At both extreme latitudes and extreme elevations, life can be hard: the air is cold, sunlight is limited, the growing season is short, and the winds can be brutal and relentless. Plants living in these habitats tend to grow close to the ground and have smaller-than-average leaves (to limit evaporation of water).

19·3–19·6 Hormones regulate growth and development.

Plant hormones are chemical signals produced by plant cells that enable the plant to respond to environmental variables and that influence its growth and development.

GIBBERELLINS

Gibberellins are a group of related hormones, produced primarily in meristems and seeds, that regulate a plant's growth processes, mainly by stimulating cell division and cell elongation.

THE PRIMARY EFFECTS OF GIBBERELLINS

SPEED SEED GERMINATION
Gibberellins initiate the production of enzymes that help break down nutrients stored within the seed's endosperm, allowing quicker and more efficient use of the seed's energy reserves.

PROMOTE STEM ELONGATION
Gibberellins affect stem elongation by increasing the distance between nodes, thus spacing the branch points farther apart.

INDUCE EARLY BLOOMING OF FLOWERS
Gibberellins can cause flower production in the absence of a triggering event from the external environment.

PROMOTE FRUIT ENLARGEMENT
Seedless grapes sprayed with large amounts of gibberellins grow larger and, due to the stem-elongation effects, have more space between the grapes on the bunch.

AUXINS

Auxins are a group of hormones found primarily in meristems and immature plant tissues that play several important roles in stimulating and regulating a plant's growth and development.

THE PRIMARY EFFECTS OF AUXINS

STIMULATE SHOOT ELONGATION
Auxins enhance the effect of gibberellins in shoot elongation.

CONTROL SEEDLING ORIENTATION
Auxins direct the growth of shoots and roots, making sure the correct ends are up and down.

STIMULATE ROOT BRANCHING
Auxins induce the formation of roots.

PROMOTE FRUIT DEVELOPMENT
Auxins produced within an embryo promote the maturation of the ovary wall and development of the fruit.

ETHYLENE

Ethylene is a gas produced in every part of a plant, and it has several important effects, including speeding up the rate at which many fruits ripen. Ethylene also hastens the aging and dropping of leaves from trees and the death of flowers at specific times.

ABSCISIC ACID

Abscisic acid is a hormone that is synthesized primarily in leaves, fruits, and root tips (but also in other plant parts). This hormone has the general effect of inhibiting growth and reproductive activities under adverse environmental conditions.

CYTOKININS

Cytokinins are produced primarily in the roots and fruits. However, they exert their influence in all parts of the plant. They usually work in conjunction with auxins to cause rapid cell division and promote primary growth, initiate new branches from lateral buds, induce seed germination, and retard leaf aging and death.

What Is LIFE? A GUIDE TO BIOLOGY Jay Phelan

18·7–18·11 Pollination, fertilization, and seed dispersal often depend on help from other organisms.

Because sexual reproduction requires two individuals, one plant must get its gametes to join with those of another. A broad array of solutions to this problem has evolved.

STRATEGIES FOR ACHIEVING POLLINATION

Plants usually utilize trickery or bribery to get the assistance of animals in carrying the male gametes to the female gametes.

BRIBERY
Plants offer something of value to an animal so that it carries pollen from one plant to another.

TRICKERY
Plants use methods of deception to trick animals into carrying pollen from one plant to another.

DOUBLE FERTILIZATION

In the process of double fertilization, there are two fusions of male and female nuclei: one produces the plant embryo and the other produces the endosperm.

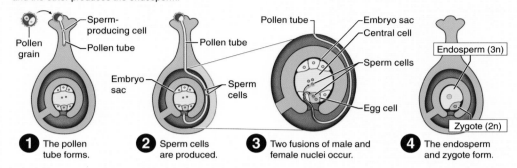

1. The pollen tube forms.
2. Sperm cells are produced.
3. Two fusions of male and female nuclei occur.
4. The endosperm and zygote form.

Labels: Sperm-producing cell, Pollen grain, Pollen tube, Embryo sac, Sperm cells, Pollen tube, Embryo sac, Central cell, Sperm cells, Egg cell, Endosperm (3n), Zygote (2n)

SEED DEVELOPMENT

Following fertilization, the ovule develops into a seed, containing a root meristem, a shoot meristem, and one or two cotyledons, surrounded by a hard casing. The seed is protected within a fruit, which aids in its dispersal.

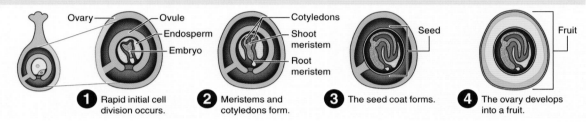

1. Rapid initial cell division occurs.
2. Meristems and cotyledons form.
3. The seed coat forms.
4. The ovary develops into a fruit.

Labels: Ovary, Ovule, Endosperm, Embryo, Cotyledons, Shoot meristem, Root meristem, Seed, Fruit

METHODS OF FRUIT AND SEED DISPERSAL

Following pollination and fertilization, plants utilize the assistance of animals, water, or wind to disperse their fruits and seeds, depositing them at new locations where the seeds can germinate and new plants can grow.

WIND-DISPERSED

HAIRY
Seeds within fruits that have bushy hairs can float in the air.

WINGED
Seeds within fruits that have wing-like structures can float away from a tree.

TINY, DUST-LIKE
Seeds that are tiny and light as dust are able to float in the air.

EXPLOSIVE
Seeds are propelled from the plant as the ripened fruits explode.

ANIMAL-DISPERSED

CARRIED
Seeds within fruits that have sharp or clingy burrs can catch on the fur of animals and be carried away.

CONSUMED
Seeds within fruits that are consumed by animals and eliminated at some distant location.

WATER-DISPERSED

Seeds within floating fruits can be dispersed by rivers or oceans.

18·12–18·15 Plants have two types of growth, usually enabling lifelong increases in length and thickness.

Primary growth makes shoots taller and roots and branches longer and forms new tissues. Secondary growth makes plants thicker and sturdier.

PRIMARY GROWTH

Primary growth occurs as a meristem cell divides, creating two new cells. One cell differentiates into a specific type of plant tissue, while the other cell remains a meristem cell, a perpetual source of new cells.

- Apical meristem cell
- Dormant meristem cell

Legend: Dermal tissue, Vascular tissue, Ground tissue

PRIMARY GROWTH AND BRANCHING
As a plant shoot grows, some meristem cells are left behind at regular intervals. The meristem cells left behind are dormant but can begin dividing at any time, pushing outward and forming the plant's branches.

SECONDARY GROWTH

Secondary growth results from cell divisions in a thin cylinder of tissue between the primary xylem and the primary phloem—the vascular cambium, a lateral meristem.

Labels: Phloem, Xylem, Vascular cambium, Secondary xylem, Secondary phloem, Pith

What Is LIFE? A GUIDE TO BIOLOGY — SECOND EDITION — **Jay Phelan**

18·1–18·3 Plants can reproduce sexually and asexually.

Most plants have two very different options for reproduction: asexual and sexual reproduction.

ASEXUAL REPRODUCTION

The process of asexual reproduction involves the growth of new, individual plants directly from the tissue of an established plant through mitosis. There are three main advantages and one disadvantage to reproducing asexually.

ENERGETICALLY EFFICIENT
No energy is wasted by producing tissues used exclusively for sexual reproduction, such as flowers, pollen, and fruit.

FASTER
Asexual reproduction dramatically increases the rate at which new individuals can be produced, enhancing an individual's fitness.

PRESERVES WINNING ALLELE COMBINATIONS
A plant that is adapted to a particular environment will pass on the same adapted set of alleles to all the individuals it produces asexually.

DISADVANTAGE OF ASEXUAL REPRODUCTION

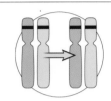

REDUCED GENETIC VARIATION
Asexually reproduced individuals are identical to their parents. This reduced variety in genetic material can leave plant populations in a vulnerable state, with a reduced capacity to evolve.

SEXUAL REPRODUCTION

Sexual reproduction enhances the genetic diversity among an individual's offspring in several important ways.

GENETIC MATERIAL COMES FROM TWO INDIVIDUALS
Offspring carry a mixture of traits from each parent plant.

RECOMBINATION DURING GAMETE PRODUCTION
Each gamete carries a mixture of alleles that have most likely never occurred before.

REASSORTMENT OF HOMOLOGUES
The homologues and sister chromatids distributed to each daughter cell during meiosis are a random mix of maternal and paternal genetic material.

18·4–18·6 Flowers have several roles in plant reproduction.

Sexually reproducing angiosperms produce flowers as the chief structure for sexual reproduction.

FLOWER STRUCTURE

Flowers can vary greatly in shape, but, with only a few exceptions, they all have the same fundamental structures: sepals, petals, stamens, and a carpel.

♀ CARPEL
Female reproductive structure

- **STIGMA**
  Sticky landing site for pollen
- **STYLE**
  Supportive stalk
- **OVARY**
  Enclosed chamber containing the ovule(s)

♂ STAMEN
Male reproductive structure

- **ANTHER**
  Site of pollen grain production
- **FILAMENT**
  Supportive stalk

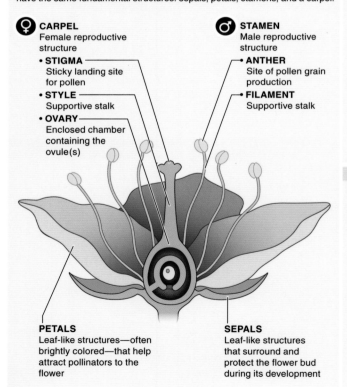

PETALS
Leaf-like structures—often brightly colored—that help attract pollinators to the flower

SEPALS
Leaf-like structures that surround and protect the flower bud during its development

MALE GAMETE DEVELOPMENT

The male reproductive structure produces pollen grains, two-cell structures that are water-tight and have a sticky surface. One of the cells forms a pollen tube, and the other produces two sperm cells.

POLLEN PRODUCTION
Pollen grains—structures that contain the male gametes—develop from the microspore mother cells located within the spore sacs of the anther.

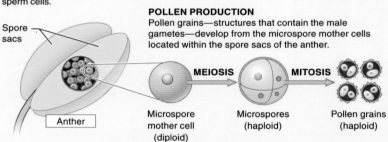

Spore sacs

Anther

MEIOSIS → **MITOSIS**

Microspore mother cell (diploid)

Microspores (haploid)

Pollen grains (haploid)

FEMALE GAMETE DEVELOPMENT

Within the ovary, diploid cells differentiate into ovules, each of which is a group of outer protective cells around a diploid egg-producing cell. The egg-producing cell undergoes meiosis to form haploid megaspores, one of which undergoes mitosis several times to produce the embryo sac, the structure that contains the egg and is the site of fertilization.

EMBRYO SAC PRODUCTION
The embryo sac—a structure that contains the female gametes—develops from the mega-spore mother cell located within an ovule.

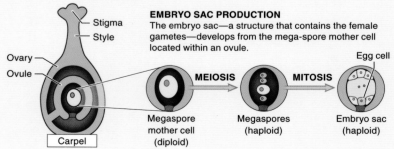

Stigma
Style
Ovary
Ovule
Carpel

MEIOSIS → **MITOSIS**

Egg cell

Megaspore mother cell (diploid)

Megaspores (haploid)

Embryo sac (haploid)

17·8–17·10 Plant nutrition: plants obtain sunlight and usable chemical elements from the environment.

Just as humans will not grow and remain healthy without a nutritious diet, plants will get sick, wither, and even die if they don't have adequate nutrition.

REQUIREMENTS FOR PLANT NUTRITION

Plant growth depends on four important factors:

 SUNLIGHT
Provides energy to build molecules of sugar

 WATER
Essential to nearly every chemical reaction within a plant

 AIR
Provides a source of carbon dioxide (for photosynthesis) and oxygen (for cellular respiration)

 SOIL
Although soil itself is not necessary, it typically contains the minerals essential for building new cells and assembling them into new tissues

These six essential minerals are required in relatively large amounts and are particularly important for plant growth and metabolism.

 N Nitrogen   **P** Phosphorus   **Mg** Magnesium

 K Potassium   **S** Sulfur   **Ca** Calcium

NITROGEN FIXATION

Among the minerals, nitrogen is the chemical that most limits plant growth, because it is required in nearly all plant cells and tissues. A mutually beneficial relationship has evolved that enables plants to gain access to nitrogen that is "fixed"—that is, chemically modified into a usable form—by bacteria.

1 Atmospheric nitrogen does not exist in an easily usable form in nature and must first be chemically modified by bacteria.

2 Bacteria break apart the strong and stable bonds of atmospheric nitrogen.

3 Nitrogen is converted into molecules with a single nitrogen atom, and is then usable by plants.

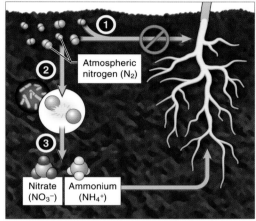

Atmospheric nitrogen (N_2)

Nitrate (NO_3^-)   Ammonium (NH_4^+)

17·11–17·13 Plants transport water, sugar, and minerals through vascular tissue.

Nutrient transport in plants occurs in two separate systems: the xylem and phloem.

WATER TRANSPORT

Xylem directs the flow of water and dissolved minerals from the roots to all other plant tissues.

1 **EVAPORATION**
Due to low water concentration in the air relative to the water concentration in the leaf, molecules of water are vaporized, one by one.

2 **TENSION**
Water molecules form hydrogen bonds with one another and these bonds cause the molecules to stick together. So as one molecule evaporates, it creates a tension, pulling on all the other water molecules that are stuck to it.

3 **COHESION**
The cohesion or stickiness of the water molecules links them together all the way down to the roots of the tree. As one molecule evaporates and pulls up the molecule next to it, that molecule pulls up the molecule next to it, and so on, all the way down to the roots.

SUGAR TRANSPORT

The phloem controls sugar movement throughout the plant in five steps.

1 Sugar is loaded by active transport into the phloem from sites of production (primarily leaves).

2 The increased sugar concentration in the phloem immediately causes water to move from the xylem into the phloem by osmosis.

3 As the water moves into the phloem, it increases the fluid pressure inside the phloem.

4 The increased phloem pressure causes the fluid in the phloem to move elsewhere in the plant, such as to the roots, much like a tube of toothpaste being squeezed.

5 As the sugar is pushed through the plant body, it is moved out of the phloem by active transport at various locations where it is needed—such as into root cells for storage and/or growth.

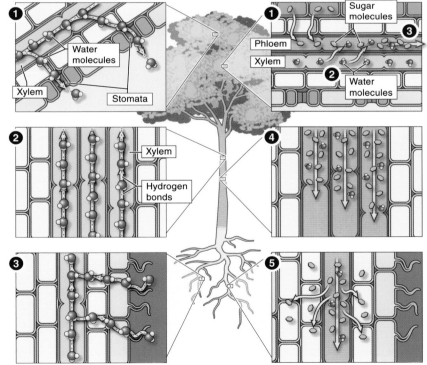

Water molecules / Xylem / Stomata / Xylem / Hydrogen bonds / Sugar molecules / Phloem / Xylem / Water molecules

17·1–17·3 Three basic tissue types give rise to diverse plant characteristics.

Plants are an extremely diverse and successful group of organisms.

VASCULAR PLANT STRUCTURE

Plants are generally composed of three distinct parts: roots, stems, and leaves.

LEAVES
• The primary site of photosynthesis, the conversion of energy from the sun into food for the plant

STEMS
• Provide structural support for the plant
• Position leaves so that they can be exposed to sunlight for photosynthesis
• Conduct food, water, and nutrients throughout the plant

ROOTS
• Absorb water and minerals from the soil
• Anchor the plant in place

MONOCOTS vs. EUDICOTS

The flowering plants are divided into two major groups, the monocots and the eudicots, based on structural features of their seeds, leaves, stems, flowers, and roots.

	SEEDS	LEAVES	STEMS	FLOWERS	ROOTS
MONOCOTS	Embryos have one cotyledon	Generally have parallel veins	Vascular tissue is arranged in scattered bundles	Flower parts typically occur in multiples of three	Generally have fibrous roots
EUDICOTS	Embryos have two cotyledons	Generally have branching veins	Vascular tissue is arranged in an orderly ring	Flower parts typically occur in multiples of four or five	Generally have a tap root

TYPES OF TISSUE IN VASCULAR PLANTS

All vascular plants are organized around the same basic body plan and built up from the same three types of tissues.

DERMAL TISSUE
Covers and protects the surface of the plant

VASCULAR TISSUE
Transports water and nutrients throughout the plant

GROUND TISSUE
Makes up the bulk of the plant and is where most of the plant's metabolic activities are carried out

Leaf cross section

Stem cross section

Root cross section

VASCULAR TISSUE

Plants have two parallel transport systems, each made from a different type of vascular tissue, that transport water, sugar, and other nutrients to where they are needed.

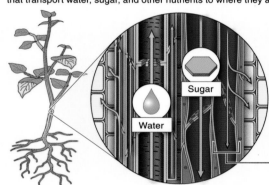

Sugar

Water

XYLEM
Conducts water and dissolved minerals absorbed by the roots to tissues throughout the plant

PHLOEM
Conducts sugar produced by photosynthesis in the leaves to tissues throughout the plant

Sieve tube

17·4–17·7 Most plants have common structural features.

The body plans of plants are organized around three structures: roots, stems and leaves.

ROOTS

Roots have three primary functions in plants: (1) absorption, the uptake of water and dissolved minerals from soil; (2) anchorage, securing the plant in place; and (3) storage of water and excess starch for future use.

Eudicot root cross section

Root hairs

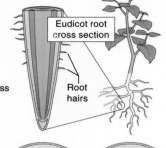

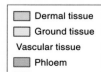 Dermal tissue
 Ground tissue
Vascular tissue
Phloem
Xylem

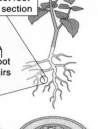

Eudicot root cross section

Monocot root cross section

STEMS

Stems provide structural support and position leaves where they can intercept sunlight.

Apical meristem

Nodes

Eudicot stem cross section

Eudicot stem cross section

Monocot stem cross section

LEAVES

Leaves are thin and have a three-layered structure that enables them to effectively capture energy and transport water and nutrients.

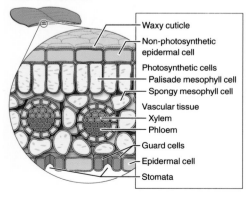

Waxy cuticle
Non-photosynthetic epidermal cell
Photosynthetic cells
Palisade mesophyll cell
Spongy mesophyll cell
Vascular tissue
Xylem
Phloem
Guard cells
Epidermal cell
Stomata

16·7–16·12 Human interference generally reduces biodiversity.

Disruptions of ecosystems can be disastrous.

EXOTIC SPECIES

PROBLEM
Exotic species can threaten native populations.

CAUSE
Exotic species are often introduced, both accidentally and intentionally, by humans. Once introduced, these species can multiply, unchecked by predation, overwhelming competitors and irreversibly altering ecosystems.

STRATEGIES FOR SOLUTION
Better regulation and restriction of intentional introductions; better vigilance against accidental introductions

ACID RAIN

PROBLEM
Acid precipitation kills plants and aquatic animals directly, and also acts indirectly via changes in soil and water chemistry.

CAUSE
Burning fossil fuels releases sulfur dioxide and nitrogen dioxide. The compounds form sulfuric and nitric acids when combined with water vapor.

STRATEGIES FOR SOLUTION
Tighter regulation and reduction of sulfur dioxide and nitrogen dioxide emissions

INCREASED GREENHOUSE GAS EMISSIONS

PROBLEM
The average temperature has increased rapidly during the past 50 years, affecting both the physical environment and the biological world.

CAUSE
Burning fossil fuels and clearing land to cultivate crops have significantly increased levels of greenhouse gases in the atmosphere.

STRATEGIES FOR SOLUTION
Reduced emissions of greenhouse gases (particularly from the burning of fossil fuels)

OZONE LAYER DEPLETION

PROBLEM
Increased levels of ultraviolet light reach the earth's surface, leading to a greater incidence of health problems in animals and decreased rates of photosynthesis in plants.

CAUSE
Synthetic chemicals known as chlorofluoro-carbons (CFCs) leak into the atmosphere, where they cause the breakdown of ozone.

STRATEGIES FOR SOLUTION
Reduced production and emission of CFCs

DEFORESTATION

PROBLEM
Tropical rain forests are being cleared at unprecedentedly high rates, endangering countless species and increasing the concentration of greenhouse gases in the atmosphere.

CAUSE
The land is cleared for agriculture, logging, gold mines, and oil wells.

STRATEGIES FOR SOLUTION
Reduced destruction of high-biodiversity habitats, particularly tropical rain forests

16·13–16·14 We can develop strategies for effective conservation.

Effective conservation requires setting goals on which elements of biodiversity (genes, species, or ecosystems) to conserve and setting priorities among those elements.

PRESERVING SPECIES VS. PRESERVING HABITATS

Most approaches to conservation biology have focused on the preservation of individual species. Increasingly, however, conservation biology is shifting toward the preservation of important habitats, focusing on conserving communities and ecosystems. This habitat-conserving approach also leads to the preservation of individual species, but it has the added benefit of preserving, at the same time, different species within a habitat, including many that have not yet been identified.

DESIGNING EFFECTIVE NATURE PRESERVES

The design of natural preserves has evolved. Modern preserves focus on the use of several design features that maximize their efficiency, including larger, rather than smaller, preserves; circular, rather than linear, preserves; and:

CORRIDORS
Strips of land that allow gene flow and reduce inbreeding among distinct populations in different larger natural preserves

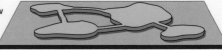

BUFFER ZONES
Areas where limited amounts of human use are permitted that surround a core natural preserve

16·1–16·4 Measuring and defining biodiversity is complex.

Defining biodiversity is difficult because it can be considered at multiple levels, from entire ecosystems to species to genes and alleles.

WHAT IS BIODIVERSITY?

Biodiversity is more than just a counting of species. It encompasses the genetic variability among organisms within a species, the variety of different species, and the variety of ecosystems on earth.

GENES AND ALLELES
The number of alleles in a species

SPECIES
The number of species in an ecosystem

ECOSYSTEMS
The number of ecosystems in a region

THE VALUE OF BIODIVERSITY

UTILITARIAN VALUE
Biodiversity can provide materials or processes that make our lives better.

AESTHETIC VALUE
Biodiversity can be beautiful to look at and pleasant to experience.

SYMBOLIC VALUE
Biodiversity can provide imagery that conveys meaningful abstract ideas.

NATURALISTIC VALUE
Biodiversity can provide the satisfaction that comes from direct contact with nature.

FACTORS THAT INFLUENCE BIODIVERSITY

SOLAR ENERGY AVAILABLE
Greater amounts of solar energy (such as near the equator), are associated with increased species richness.

EVOLUTIONARY HISTORY OF AN AREA
Communities diversify over time. The more time that passes without a climatic event, such as an ice age, the greater the diversity in an area.

RATE OF DISTURBANCE
A habitat with an intermediate amount of disturbance tends to have the greatest species richness.

BIODIVERSITY HOTSPOTS

Biodiversity hotspots are regions of significant biodiversity under threat of destruction. There are 25 biodiversity hotspots around the world; they cover less than 1% of the world's area, but have 20% or more of the world's species.

16·5–16·6 Extinction reduces biodiversity.

An extinction occurs when all individuals in a species have died.

TWO CATEGORIES OF EXTINCTIONS

Extinctions generally fall into two categories:

● **MASS EXTINCTIONS**
A large number of species (even entire families) become extinct over a short period of time due to extraordinary and sudden environmental change.

● **BACKGROUND EXTINCTIONS**
These extinctions occur at lower rates during times other than mass extinctions.

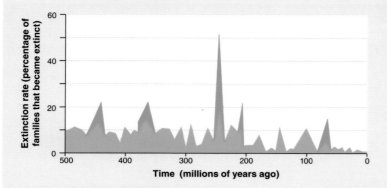

FACTORS THAT INFLUENCE THE RISK OF BACKGROUND EXTINCTION

GEOGRAPHIC RANGE:
EXTENSIVE vs. RESTRICTED
Species restricted in their range are more vulnerable than those with extensive ranges.

LOCAL POPULATION SIZE:
LARGE vs. SMALL
Species with small population sizes are at increased risk of extinction.

HABITAT TOLERANCE:
BROAD vs. NARROW
Species with narrow habitat tolerances are at greater risk of extinction than species with broader habitat tolerances.

CURRENT MASS EXTINCTION

Most biologists believe that we are currently in the midst of a mass extinction, that it is the result of human activities, and that it poses a serious threat to the future survival of humans.

15·6–15·8 Energy and chemicals flow within ecosystems.

Energy from the sun flows through ecosystems while chemicals repeatedly cycle from the physical environment through living organisms and back into the environment.

ENERGY FLOW THROUGH THE ECOSYSTEM

Energy from the sun is intercepted and converted into chemical energy, which passes through an ecosystem in about four stops, known as trophic levels. At each step, some usable energy is lost as heat.

Sun

PRIMARY PRODUCERS
Plants convert light energy from the sun into food through photosynthesis.

PRIMARY CONSUMERS
Herbivores are animals that eat plants.

SECONDARY CONSUMERS
Carnivores are animals that eat herbivores.

TERTIARY CONSUMERS
Top carnivores are animals that eat other carnivores.

This linear pathway is overly simplified. In actuality, food webs are often a better representation; many organisms (including you, if you eat vegetables and meat) can occupy more than one position in the chain.

INEFFICIENT ENERGY FLOW

Only about 10% of the biomass from each trophic level is converted into biomass in the next trophic level. The rest of the available energy is lost to the environment, a consequence of several factors, including non-predatory deaths, incomplete digestion of prey/food, and respiration.

CHEMICAL CYCLES

Chemicals essential to life—including carbon, nitrogen, and phosphorus—cycle through ecosystems. They are usually captured from the atmosphere, soil, or water by growing organisms, passed from one trophic level to the next as organisms eat other organisms, and returned to the environment through respiration, decomposition, and erosion. These cycles can be disrupted as human activities significantly increase the amounts of chemicals added to soils for use by plants or released to the environment.

15·9–15·14 Species interactions influence the structure of communities.

Interacting species in a community coevolve in a variety of ways, some antagonistic and others mutually beneficial.

NICHE FEATURES

An organism's niche encompasses the following features:
- The space an organism requires
- The type and amount of food an organism utilizes
- The timing of an organism's reproduction
- An organism's temperature and moisture requirements and other necessary living conditions
- The organisms for which it is a food source
- Its influence on competitors

COMPETITION: WHEN NICHES OVERLAP

When the fundamental niches of two species overlap, the species compete and two outcomes are possible:

or

COMPETITIVE EXCLUSION
One species within the niche utilizes resources more efficiently, driving the other species to local extinction.

RESOURCE PARTITIONING
The species each alter their use of the niche, dividing the resources.

BENEFICIAL SPECIES INTERACTIONS

In commensalism, one species benefits and the other is neither harmed nor helped. In mutualism, both species benefit from the interaction.

PARASITISM

Parasitism is a symbiotic relationship in which one organism benefits while the other is harmed.

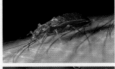

ECTOPARASITES
Parasites that live on their host

ENDOPARASITES
Parasites that live inside their host

DEFENSES FOR REDUCING PREDATION

PHYSICAL DEFENSE
Includes mechanical, chemical, warning coloration, and camouflage mechanisms

BEHAVIORAL DEFENSE
Includes hiding or escaping, and alarm calling or fighting back

15·15–15·16 Communities can change or remain stable over time.

Most communities change over time. The patterns of succession depend on the rate and magnitude of disturbances.

SUCCESSION

Succession is the change in the species composition of a community over time, following a disturbance.

PRIMARY SUCCESSION
Primary succession begins after a disturbance leaves an area barren of soil and with no life.

SECONDARY SUCCESSION
Secondary succession is like primary succession with a head start. It begins when a disturbance opens up part of a community to the development and growth of species previously outcompeted by other species in the area.

KEYSTONE SPECIES

Keystone species have a relatively large influence on the number and types of species present. When a keystone species is removed from the community, the species mix changes dramatically. For this reason, preserving keystone species is an important strategy in preserving biodiversity.

What Is LIFE? SECOND EDITION A GUIDE TO BIOLOGY **Jay Phelan**

15 ECOSYSTEMS and COMMUNITIES...to go

15·1–15·2 Ecosystems have living and non-living components.

An ecosystem is a community of biological organisms plus the non-living components in the environment with which the organisms interact.

ECOSYSTEMS

All ecosystems share two essential features:

BIOTIC ENVIRONMENT
• The living organisms within an area (often referred to as a community)

PHYSICAL (ABIOTIC) ENVIRONMENT
• The chemical resources and physical conditions within an area (often referred to as the organisms' habitat)

TERRESTRIAL BIOMES

Terrestrial biomes—large ecosystems that cover huge geographic areas—are determined by the temperature and amounts of precipitation in conjunction with the magnitude of seasonal variation in these factors.

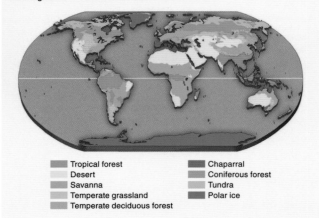

Tropical forest	Chaparral
Desert	Coniferous forest
Savanna	Tundra
Temperate grassland	Polar ice
Temperate deciduous forest	

AQUATIC BIOMES

Aquatic biomes are determined by physical features, including salinity, water movement, and depth.

Lakes and ponds
Rivers and streams
Estuaries and wetlands
Open oceans
Coral reefs

15·3–15·5 Interacting physical forces create weather.

Global patterns of weather are largely determined by the earth's round shape.

THE DISTRIBUTION OF SOLAR ENERGY

Solar energy hits the equator at a more direct angle than at the Poles, leading to warmer temperatures at lower latitudes.

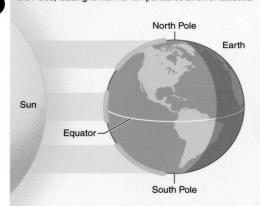

THE FORMATION OF RAIN

1 When solar heat hits the earth, it warms the air at that point. The heated air rises.

2 As hot air rises, getting farther from the warm earth, it cools.

3 Because cold air holds less moisture than warm air, clouds form and rain falls.

THE FORMATION OF DESERTS

Large circulating masses of air are responsible for many of the large-scale rainfall patterns throughout the world. Air heated by the sun rises, expands northward and southward, and moves back toward earth as it cools. As the air moves down toward earth's surface and becomes warmer, it can hold more and more moisture, causing these areas to have very little rainfall.

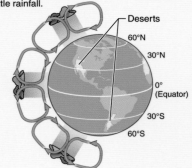

THE RAIN SHADOW EFFECT

With higher elevation, the temperature drops. On the windward side of mountains, rainfall is high as the colder air releases moisture; on the back side, descending air becomes warmer and can hold more moisture. This reduces rainfall, causing rain shadow deserts.

MODERN LANDSCAPES

Urban development increases the absorption of solar energy, leading to higher temperatures, and creates wind near the bottom of tall buildings.

OCEAN CIRCULATION PATTERNS

There are several large, circular patterns of flowing water in the oceans due to a combination of forces including wind, the earth's rotation, the gravitational pull of the moon, temperature, and salt concentration.

These circular patterns are responsible for the water off the west coast of the U.S. being much colder than the water off the east coast of the U.S.

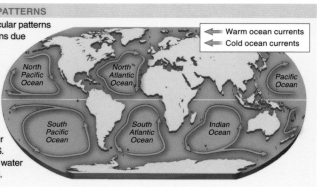

Warm ocean currents
Cold ocean currents

What Is LIFE? A GUIDE TO BIOLOGY
Jay Phelan
SECOND EDITION

14·10–14·12 Ecology influences the evolution of aging in a population.

From a population perspective, aging is an increased risk of dying with increasing age, after reaching the age of maturity.

NATURAL SELECTION AND AGING

Natural selection cannot weed out harmful alleles that do not diminish an individual's reproductive output relative to other individuals in a population. Consequently, those harmful alleles accumulate in the genomes of individuals of nearly all species. This leads to the multiple physiological breakdowns that we see as aging.

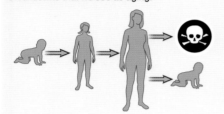

ENVIRONMENTAL RISKS AND AGING

The rate of aging and pattern of mortality are determined by the hazard factor of the organism's environment. In environments characterized by low mortality risk, populations of slowly aging individuals with long life spans evolve. In environments characterized by high mortality risk, populations of early-aging, short-lived individuals evolve.

HIGH HAZARD FACTOR
• Relatively high risk of death at each age
• Individuals tend to reproduce earlier
• Earlier aging
• Shorter life spans

Rodent

2 years

Longevity

LOW HAZARD FACTOR
• Relatively low risk of death at each age
• Individuals tend to reproduce later
• Later aging
• Longer life spans

Tortoise

150 years

Longevity

14·13–14·15 The human population is growing rapidly.

In humans, current birth rates exceed death rates by so much that we add 80 million people to the world population each year!

AGE PYRAMIDS

Age pyramids show the number of individuals in a population within each age group at one point in time. They give us a snapshot of the age-structure of a population and allow us to estimate birth and death rates over multi-year periods.

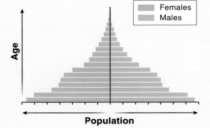

Females
Males

Age — **Population**

Age — **Population**

Industrialized countries have age pyramids that appear more rectangular in shape, due to low birth rates and the low death rates in older individuals.

Developing countries have age pyramids that appear triangular in shape, due to high birth rates and the high death rates in older individuals.

DEMOGRAPHIC TRANSITION

The demographic transition tends to occur with the industrialization of countries. It is characterized by an initial reduction in the death rate, followed later by a reduction in the birth rate.

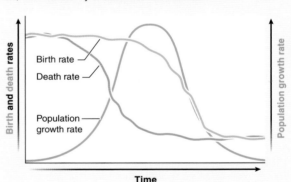

Birth and death rates

Birth rate
Death rate

Population growth rate

Population growth rate

Time

HUMAN POPULATION GROWTH

The world's human population is currently growing at a very high rate, but limited resources will eventually limit this growth, most likely at a population size between 7 and 11 billion.

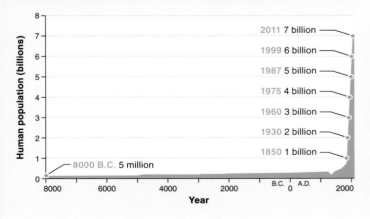

2011 7 billion
1999 6 billion
1987 5 billion
1975 4 billion
1960 3 billion
1930 2 billion
1850 1 billion
8000 B.C. 5 million

Human population (billions) — Year
B.C. 0 A.D.

INCREASING THE CARRYING CAPACITY FOR THE HUMAN POPULATION

One reason that the carrying capacity for the human population is difficult to estimate is that we can increase it in a variety of ways.

EXPANDING INTO NEW HABITATS
With fire, tools, shelter, and efficient food distribution, we can survive almost anywhere on earth.

INCREASING THE AGRICULTURAL PRODUCTIVITY OF THE LAND
With fertilizers, mechanized agricultural methods, and selection for higher yields, fewer people can now produce much more food than was previously thought possible.

FINDING WAYS TO LIVE AT HIGHER DENSITIES
Public health and civil engineering advances make it possible for higher and higher densities of people to live together with minimal problems from waste and infectious diseases.

What Is LIFE? SECOND EDITION
A GUIDE TO BIOLOGY
Jay Phelan

14·1–14·6 Population ecology is the study of how populations interact with their environments.

Population ecology examines features that cannot be studied on an individual organism, such as population size and growth rates.

WHAT IS ECOLOGY?

Ecology is the study of interactions between organisms and their environments. It can be studied at many levels, including:

INDIVIDUALS
Individual organisms

POPULATIONS
Groups of individual organisms that interbreed with each other

COMMUNITIES
Populations of different species that interact with each other within a locale

ECOSYSTEMS
All living organisms, as well as non-living elements, that interact in a particular area

Population ecology is the study of the interactions between populations of organisms and their environments, particularly their patterns of growth and how they are influenced by other species and by environmental factors.

POPULATION GROWTH

Populations tend to grow exponentially until limited resources cause the growth to slow to logistic rates.

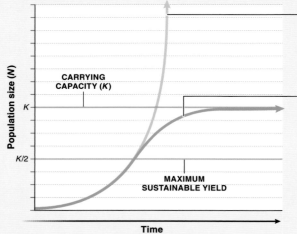

CARRYING CAPACITY (*K*)

MAXIMUM SUSTAINABLE YIELD

Population size (*N*)

K

K/2

Time

EXPONENTIAL GROWTH
Exponential growth describes a population growing at a rate proportional to its size in other words, the bigger the population the faster it grows. Exponential growth cannot continue indefinitely (population sizes would quickly exceed available resources).

LOGISTIC GROWTH
Logistic growth describes population growth that is gradually reduced as the population nears the environment's carrying capacity.

Although the logistic growth pattern is a useful and good approximation of the general growth pattern of many populations, some populations cycle between periods of rapid growth and rapid shrinkage.

LIMITING POPULATION GROWTH

A population's growth can be reduced both by **density dependent factors** related to crowding, such as food supply, habitat for living and breeding, parasite and disease risk, and predation risk, and by **density independent factors** such as natural or human-caused environmental calamities.

MAXIMUM SUSTAINABLE YIELD

Efficient and sustainable management of natural resources requires the determination of a population's maximum sustainable yield, the point at which the maximum number of individuals are being added to the population (and so can be harvested or utilized).

14·7–14·9 A life history is like a species summary.

An organism's pattern of investment in growth, reproduction, and survival is described by its life history.

VARIATION IN LIFE HISTORIES

Strategies for reproducing vary widely across different species. These range from investing in just one (very intensive) episode of reproduction to making numerous smaller investments over a long period of time.

Three examples of very different life history strategies include:

Antechinus
(BIG-BANG REPRODUCTION)
• Reaches sexual maturity at one year
• Mates intensely over a three-week period
• Males die shortly after mating period
• Females usually die after weaning their first litter

Greater bulldog bat
(SLOW, GRADUAL REPRODUCTIVE INVESTMENT)
• Reaches sexual maturity at one year
• Produces about one offspring per year

House mouse
(FAST, INTENSIVE REPRODUCTIVE INVESTMENT)
• Reaches sexual maturity at one month
• Produces litters of six to ten offspring every month

LIFE TABLES

Life tables summarize life and death of a species. Shown here: a life table for the cactus ground finch.

AGE (beginning of interval)	NUMBER ALIVE (beginning of interval)	PROPORTION ALIVE (beginning of interval)	DEATHS DURING INTERVAL	PROBABILITY OF DYING DURING INTERVAL
0	210	1.00	140	0.67
3	70	0.33	28	0.40
6	42	0.20	28	0.67
9	14	0.07	10	0.71
12	4	0.02	4	1.00
15	0	0.00	n/a	n/a

The data here reveal an approximately constant probability of dying during each age interval, characteristic of a Type II survivorship curve.

SURVIVORSHIP CURVES

Survivorship curves show the proportion of individuals of a particular age that are alive in a population.

Proportion of individuals in population that survive

Age

TYPE I
High survivorship until old age, then rapidly decreasing survivorship

TYPE II
Survivorship decreases at a steady, regular pace

TYPE III
High mortality early in life, but those that survive the early years live long lives

What Is LIFE? A GUIDE TO BIOLOGY
Jay Phelan

13·10–13·12 Archaea exploit some of the most extreme habitats.

Although archaea resemble bacteria, evolutionarily they are more closely related to the eukarya.

ARCHAEA STRUCTURE

Although archaea and bacteria are similar in appearance (and both domains are prokaryotes), they have significant differences in their DNA sequences, as well as differences in their plasma membranes, cell walls, and flagella.

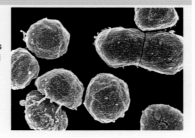

ARCHAEA THRIVE IN EXTREME CONDITIONS

Some archaea can tolerate extreme physical and chemical conditions that are impossible for most other living organisms, while others live in moderate conditions and even in the human intestine.

POTENTIAL USES OF ARCHAEA

Because some archaea are able to efficiently degrade hydrocarbons, it may someday be possible to utilize them in the removal of sludge that accumulates in oil refinery tanks and in the cleanup of contaminated environments such as oil slicks.

13·13–13·15 Most protists are single-celled eukaryotes.

The nucleus is an evolutionary innovation that appeared for the first time in protists.

EARLY PROTISTS

The earliest eukaryotic organisms—having internal structures, called cellular organelles, that performed specialized activities—were protists. Protist-resembling fossils have been found in rock 1.9 billion years old.

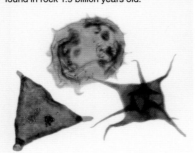

DIVERSITY OF PROTISTS

ANIMAL-LIKE PROTISTS
Some protists, such as *Trichomonas vaginalis* shown here, move around and hunt for prey, much as an animal might.

FUNGI-LIKE PROTISTS
Some protists, such as the plasmodial slime mold shown here, live as heterotrophs and form sheet-like colonies of cells that resemble a fungus.

PLANT-LIKE PROTISTS
Some protists, such as the kelp forest shown here, are multicellular and photosynthetic, resembling a plant.

13·16–13·9 Viruses are at the border between living and non-living.

A virus is not alive, but it can carry out some of the same functions as living organisms, provided that it can get inside a cell.

BASIC STRUCTURE OF A VIRUS

All viruses have a container (the capsid) that holds their genetic material, and sometimes the capsid is wrapped in a membrane (an envelope).

- Capsid (container made of protein)
- Genetic material (DNA or RNA)
- Plasma membrane (envelope)
- Glycoproteins

VIRAL REPLICATION

1. After the virus binds to the host cell's membrane, the viral DNA is taken into the cell.

2. Viral DNA is replicated into dozens of new copies, using the host's metabolic machinery and energy.

3. Viral mRNA is transcribed from the viral DNA.

4. New viral proteins are synthesized, again using the host's protein-production molecules.

5. The new viral DNA and proteins assemble, forming many new virus particles.

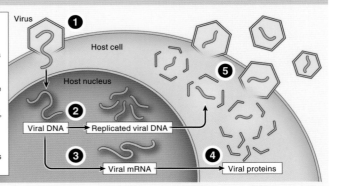

Virus
Host cell
Host nucleus
Viral DNA → Replicated viral DNA
Viral mRNA
Viral proteins

VIRUSES AND HEALTH

Many diseases are caused by viruses. Some viral diseases, such as the common cold, are not usually serious, but others have been responsible for worldwide epidemics, called pandemics. The influenza pandemic of 1918–1919 killed at least 20 million people, and possibly as many as 50 million. In the current HIV/AIDS pandemic, nearly 40 million people have been infected, with an annual mortality of about 3 million.

HIV

Infection by the retrovirus HIV is especially difficult to control. High rates of mutation continually change the properties of the virus, hindering recognition by the immune system. Additionally, the high rate of mutations commonly causes the production of variants that are resistant to the drugs used to treat the HIV infection.

13·1–13·2 There are microbes in all three domains.

Microbes are the simplest but probably also the most successful organisms on earth.

MICROBES IN THE TREE OF LIFE

Microbes are grouped together only because they are small, not because of evolutionary relatedness. They occur in all three domains of life, and also include the viruses.

VIRUSES
Viruses aren't truly living organisms and they are not classified into any of the three domains.

DOMAIN BACTERIA	DOMAIN ARCHAEA	DOMAIN EUKARYA

Neisseria meningitidis, a bacterium that can cause meningitis

Haloferax mediterranei, an extremely halophilic archaean

A giant amoeba, from the genus *Pelomyxa*

13·3–13·5 Bacteria may be the most diverse of all organisms.

Different species of bacteria are found virtually everywhere and can eat virtually anything.

BACTERIA STRUCTURE

Bacteria are single-celled organisms, with an envelope surrounding the cytoplasm, which contains the DNA (they have no nuclei and no intracellular organelles).

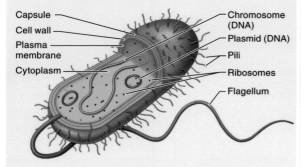

Capsule
Cell wall
Plasma membrane
Cytoplasm

Chromosome (DNA)
Plasmid (DNA)
Pili
Ribosomes
Flagellum

CELL DIVISION IN BACTERIA

Bacteria divide by binary fission, creating two new daughter cells that each carry the genetic information that was present in the chromosome of the mother cell. Bacterial populations can grow rapidly—with some bacteria able to divide every 20 minutes.

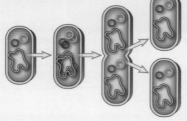

METHODS OF GENETIC EXCHANGE IN BACTERIA WITHIN THE SAME GENERATION

CONJUGATION
A bacterium transfers a copy of some or all of its DNA to another bacterium.

TRANSDUCTION
A virus containing pieces of bacterial DNA inadvertently picked up from its previous host infects a new bacterium, passing new bacterial genes to the bacterium.

TRANSFORMATION
A bacterium can take up DNA from its surroundings (usually from bacteria that have died).

METABOLIC DIVERSITY AMONG BACTERIA

Some bacteria eat organic molecules, some eat minerals, and still others carry out photosynthesis. Some require oxygen to live, others do not.

13·6–13·9 In humans, bacteria can have harmful or beneficial health effects.

Bacterial effects on human health vary widely. Many are beneficial and many are neutral, while some can be harmful.

BENEFICIAL BACTERIA

Many bacteria are beneficial. Those living in yogurt, for example, can take up residence in your digestive tract and improve your extraction of nutrients from food while also producing vitamins. Bacteria are also used in the production of many other foods, including cheeses, and (along with yeasts) beer, wine, and vinegar.

HARMFUL BACTERIA

Some bacteria always cause disease, and others do no harm except under certain conditions. For example, *Streptococcus pyogenes* can be harmless, but under some conditions it releases toxins that are responsible for strep throat, scarlet fever, and necrotizing fasciitis (caused by the flesh-eating strains).

ANTIBIOTIC RESISTANCE

Antibiotic resistance routinely evolves in microbes. Excessive use of antibiotics in medicine and agriculture has made several of the most important pathogenic bacteria resistant to every known antibiotic, and infections caused by these bacteria are nearly impossible to treat.

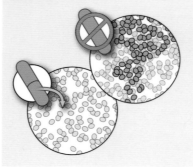

SEXUALLY TRANSMITTED DISEASES

Sexually transmitted diseases (STDs) are caused by a variety of organisms, including bacteria, viruses, protists, fungi, and arthropods. Worldwide, more than 300 million people are newly infected each year.

BACTERIUM
• Gonorrhea
• Syphilis
• Chlamydia

PROTIST
• Trichomoniasis

VIRUS
• HIV/AIDS
• Genital herpes
• Human papilloma virus (HPV)

FUNGUS
• Yeast infections

ARTHROPOD
• Crab lice

12·8–12·10 Flowering plants are the most diverse and successful plants.

Flowering plants (angiosperms) appeared in the Cretaceous period, over 100 million years ago, and diversified rapidly to become the dominant plants in the modern world.

ANGIOSPERMS

COMMON CHARACTERISTICS
- Distribute water and nutrients throughout the plant with a "circulatory system" of vascular tissue
- Produce flowers, which produce gametes
- Produce seeds that are enclosed within an ovule

MEMBERS INCLUDE
- Flowering trees, bushes, herbs, and grasses (about 250,000 species)

FLOWERS AND THEIR POLLINATORS

Angiosperms have found a way to transfer pollen from the anthers of one flower to the stigma of another: let an animal carry it (although in some cases they rely instead on wind or water). Flowers are conspicuous structures that advertise their presence with colors, shapes, patterns, and odors. Using flowers, most angiosperms are able to trick or bribe animals into transporting male gametes to female gametes, where fertilization can occur.

FLOWER STRUCTURE

♂ STAMEN
Male reproductive structure

ANTHER
Produces pollen

FILAMENT
Supporting stalk

♀ CARPEL
Female reproductive structure

STIGMA
Sticky tip

STYLE
Elongated stalk

OVARY
Contains the ovules

Petal

Sepal

12·11–12·12 Plants and animals have a love-hate relationship.

Overcoming a challenge of immobility, plants often use the assistance of animals to disperse their seeds, and have a wide range of defenses against herbivorous animals.

SEED DISPERSAL

Following pollination and fertilization, plants often enlist animals to disperse their fruits, which contain the fertilized seeds, depositing them at a new location where the seedlings can grow. Fruits are made from the ovary and, occasionally, some surrounding tissue.

PLANT DEFENSES

Plants have a wide range of defenses against herbivorous animals: from physical defenses such as thorns to chemicals that have complex effects on animals' physiology. Plants respond to insect attack by synthesizing chemicals that make the plant less palatable. Some plants living in soil that is deficient in nitrogen have switched roles, preying on insects.

12·13–12·15 Fungi and plants are partners but not close relatives.

Most fungi are multicellular, sessile decomposers.

WHAT IS A FUNGUS?
The defining characteristics of fungi.

FUNGI ARE DECOMPOSERS OR SYMBIONTS
Fungi acquire energy by breaking down the tissues of dead organisms or by absorbing nutrients from living organisms.

FUNGI ARE SESSILE
Fungi are anchored to the organic material on which they feed.

FUNGI HAVE CELL WALLS MADE OF CHITIN
Fungi have cell walls made of chitin, a chemical that is also important in producing the exoskeleton of insects.

FUNGI CLASSIFICATION
DNA sequence analyses reveal that fungi are more closely related to animals than they are to plants.

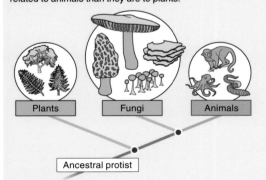

Plants

Fungi

Animals

Ancestral protist

LIFE HISTORY OF FUNGI

Fungi are decomposers, and all they need to thrive is organic material to consume and a moist environment so their hyphae don't dry out. Fungi can grow almost anywhere that is moist, and they can attain enormous sizes. Fungi have complex life cycles, with both sexual and asexual phases, and the parts of a fungus that are most often visible are its temporary spore-producing bodies.

MYCORRHIZAE
Mycorrhizal fungi grow in association with the roots of plants, receiving sugar from the plant while transferring nitrogen and phosphorus from the soil to the plant.

Hyphae

Root hair

What Is LIFE? SECOND EDITION A GUIDE TO BIOLOGY **Jay Phelan**

12·1 Plants are just one branch of the eukarya.

Plants are photosynthetic, multicellular organisms that spend most of their lives anchored in one place by their roots.

WHAT IS A PLANT?

The defining characteristics of a plant.

PLANTS CREATE THEIR OWN FOOD
Almost all plants carry out photosynthesis, using energy from sunlight to convert carbon dioxide and water into sugar.

PLANTS ARE SESSILE AND (MOSTLY) TERRESTRIAL
Plants are anchored in place at their bases and occur almost exclusively on land.

PLANTS ARE MULTICELLULAR
Plants consist of multiple cells and have structures that are specialized for different functions.

PHYLOGENY OF THE PLANTS

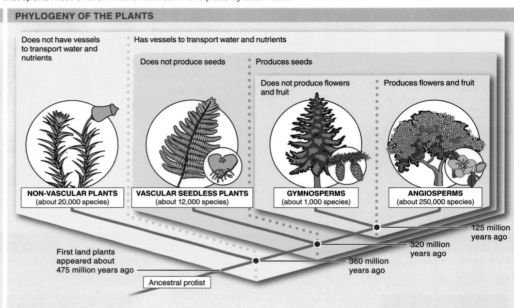

Does not have vessels to transport water and nutrients

Has vessels to transport water and nutrients

Does not produce seeds

Produces seeds

Does not produce flowers and fruit

Produces flowers and fruit

NON-VASCULAR PLANTS (about 20,000 species)

VASCULAR SEEDLESS PLANTS (about 12,000 species)

GYMNOSPERMS (about 1,000 species)

ANGIOSPERMS (about 250,000 species)

First land plants appeared about 475 million years ago

Ancestral protist

360 million years ago

320 million years ago

125 million years ago

12·2–12·4 The first plants had neither roots nor seeds.

The first land plants were small, had no leaves, roots, or flowers, and could grow only near water.

MOVING ONTO LAND PRESENTS CHALLENGES

When plants emerged onto land, they faced the same two challenges that terrestrial animals faced 25 million years later.

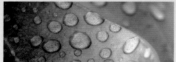

PROBLEM: GRAVITY
SOLUTION: The earliest plants grew very close to the ground, as mosses do today, in order to resist the pull of gravity.

PROBLEM: DESICCATION
SOLUTION: Plants developed an outer waxy layer called a cuticle that covers their entire surface.

NON-VASCULAR PLANTS

COMMON CHARACTERISTICS
- Distribute water and nutrients throughout plant by diffusion
- Release haploid spores, which grow and produce gametes
- Life cycle with multicellular haploid and diploid phases

MEMBERS INCLUDE
- Mosses (about 12,000 species)
- Liverworts (about 8,000 species)
- Hornworts (about 100 species)

VASCULAR SEEDLESS PLANTS

COMMON CHARACTERISTICS
- Distribute water and nutrients throughout the plant with a "circulatory system" of vascular tissue
- Release haploid spores, dispersed by the wind, which grow and produce gametes
- Life cycle (unlike in animals) with multicellular haploid and diploid phases

MEMBERS INCLUDE
- Ferns (about 12,000 species)
- Horsetails (about 15 species)

12·5–12·7 The advent of the seed opened new worlds to plants.

A seed, which contains a multicellular embryo and a store of nutrients, is a way for plants to give their offspring a good start in life.

SEEDS: STRUCTURE AND GROWTH

STRUCTURE
Fertilization produces a diploid seed, which contains a multicellular embryo and a store of carbohydrate (endosperm) to fuel its initial growth.

Protective coating
Endosperm
Embryo

GROWTH
A seedling draws energy from the endosperm while it extends its leaves upward to begin photosynthesis and its roots downward into the soil to reach water and nutrients.

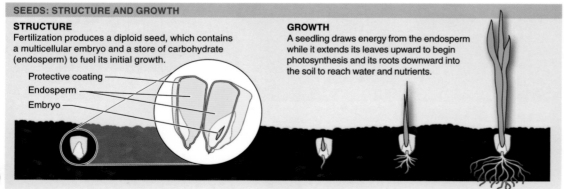

GYMNOSPERMS

COMMON CHARACTERISTICS
- Distribute water and nutrients throughout the plant with vascular tissue
- Reproductive structures called cones produce the gametes
- Fertilization produces seeds

MEMBERS INCLUDE
- Conifers (about 600 species)
- Cycads (about 300 species)
- Gnetophytes (about 65 species)
- Ginkgo (1 species)

What Is LIFE? A GUIDE TO BIOLOGY
SECOND EDITION
Jay Phelan

11·13–11·15 The phylum Chordata includes vertebrates, animals with a backbone.

All chordates have four characteristic structures: a notochord, a dorsal hollow nerve cord, pharyngeal slits, and a post-anal tail.

THE CHORDATES

COMMON CHARACTERISTICS

All chordates possess four common body structures, although in many chordates, these structures are only present during specific life stages.

- Notochord
- Dorsal hollow nerve cord
- Pharyngeal slits
- Post-anal tail

MEMBERS INCLUDE

- Tunicates (about 2,000 species)
- Lancelets (about 20 species)
- Vertebrates (about 56,000 species)

THE DISTINCT BODY STRUCTURES OF CHORDATES

NOTOCHORD

A rod of tissue extending from the head to the tail
- Simpler chordates retain the notochord throughout life
- In more complex chordates, the notochord in early embryos is replaced by a backbone

DORSAL HOLLOW NERVE CORD

Nerve cord that extends along the animal's back (its dorsal side)
- In vertebrates, the nerve cord eventually forms the spinal cord and brain

PHARYNGEAL SLITS

Slits through which water is passed in order to breathe and feed
- In many chordates (including humans), the slits disappear during embryonic development.

POST-ANAL TAIL

Tail that extends beyond the posterior (back) end of the digestive system
- Some vertebrates (including humans) have a tail only briefly, during embryonic development

FROM WATER TO LAND

The transition of vertebrates from life in water to life on land required overcoming three main obstacles. Four major evolutionary innovations allowed for this transition.

PROBLEM: RESPIRATION

Aquatic animals use gills to acquire dissolved oxygen from water. The transition onto land required the ability to breathe air.

SOLUTION: LUNGS

Gas exchange was transferred from gills to lungs, which evolved from the swim bladder found in ray-finned fishes.

PROBLEM: GRAVITY

The transition onto land required structural support to resist the pull of gravity.

SOLUTION: LIMBS and MODIFIED VERTEBRAE

Limbs evolved from the jointed fins found on the underside of lobe-finned fishes. Vertebrae were modified to transmit the body weight through the limbs to the ground.

PROBLEM: EGG DESICCATION

The transition onto land required an egg that resisted drying out when exposed to air.

SOLUTION: AMNIOTIC EGG

Terrestrial animals developed a waterproof eggshell, which prevents eggs from drying out before hatching.

11·16–11·20 All terrestrial vertebrates are tetrapods.

Terrestrial vertebrates include amphibians, reptiles (including birds), and mammals.

THE TERRESTRIAL VERTEBRATES

AMPHIBIANS
- Most species live on land as adults, but develop in water.
- Body temperature is controlled by external conditions, such as air temperature (exothermic)
- Includes frogs and toads (about 5,400 species), salamanders (about 550 species), and caecilians (170 species)

REPTILES
- Skin is covered in scales
- Body temperature is controlled by external conditions, such as air temperature (exothermic)
- Includes snakes and lizards (about 8,000 species), turtles (about 300 species), crocodiles and alligators (23 species), and tuatara (2 species)

BIRDS
- Skin is covered in feathers, enabling flight and providing insulation
- Body temperature is maintained by heat generated from cellular respiration (endothermic)
- Include about 9,700 species

MAMMALS
- Skin is covered in hair
- Body temperature is maintained by heat generated from cellular respiration (endothermic)
- Produce milk for their young
- Includes placental mammals (about 4,500 species), marsupials (about 300 species), and monotremes (5 species)

LIFE IN THE TREES

Many of the anatomical characteristics of humans and the other primates can be traced to our arboreal origins.

EYES

Forward-directed eyes and binocular vision allow for distances to be judged accurately.

ARMS

Shoulder and elbow joints allow our arms to rotate.

FINGERS AND TOES

The retention of ten fingers and ten toes allows us to grasp objects.

HUMAN EVOLUTION

Modern humans evolved in Africa between 200,000 and 100,000 years ago, and all living humans are descended from that evolutionary radiation. The evolutionary success of humans can be traced to an increase in brain size, possibly in conjunction with an omnivorous diet and increased caloric intake.

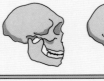

Time

What Is LIFE? SECOND EDITION — A GUIDE TO BIOLOGY — **Jay Phelan**

11 ANIMAL DIVERSIFICATION...*to go*

11·1–11·3 Animals are just one branch of the Eukarya domain.

Animals are multicellular organisms that feed on other organisms and can move during at least one stage of their life.

WHAT IS AN ANIMAL?

Three characteristics are common to all animals.

ANIMALS EAT OTHER ORGANISMS
All animals acquire energy by consuming other organisms.

ANIMALS MOVE
All animals have the ability to move—at least at some stage of their life cycle.

ANIMALS ARE MULTICELLULAR
Animals consist of multiple cells, and they generally have body parts that are specialized for different activities.

FOUR KEY DISTINCTIONS DIVIDE THE ANIMALS

The nine groups of animals in this figure represent just 25% of all animal phyla but contain 99% of all animal species.

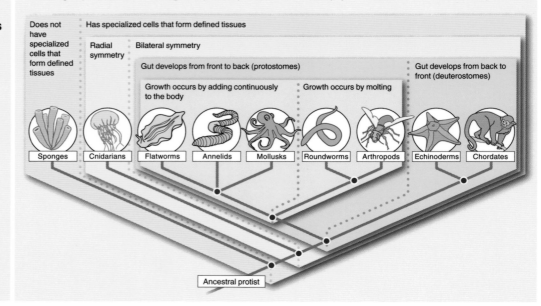

Does not have specialized cells that form defined tissues

Has specialized cells that form defined tissues

Radial symmetry

Bilateral symmetry

Gut develops from front to back (protostomes)

Gut develops from back to front (deuterostomes)

Growth occurs by adding continuously to the body

Growth occurs by molting

Sponges | Cnidarians | Flatworms | Annelids | Mollusks | Roundworms | Arthropods | Echinoderms | Chordates

Ancestral protist

11·5–11·12 Across several evolutionary transitions, the invertebrate animals diversified.

Invertebrates, defined as animals without a backbone, are the largest and most diverse group of animals, comprising 96% of all living animal species. The invertebrates are not a monophyletic group, however, and include protostomes and some (but not all) of the deuterostomes.

THE SPONGES

COMMON CHARACTERISTICS
- No tissues or organs
- Body consists of a hollow tube with pores in its wall
- Feed by pumping in water, along with bacteria, algae, and small particles of organic material, through their pores
- Free-swimming larvae
- Sessile as adults

MEMBERS INCLUDE
- About 5,000 species

THE CNIDARIANS

COMMON CHARACTERISTICS
- Radially symmetrical
- Tentacles armed with rows of stinging cells, used to paralyze prey

MEMBERS INCLUDE
- Jellyfishes
- Sea anemones
- Corals

THE FLATWORMS

COMMON CHARACTERISTICS
- Well-defined head and tail regions
- Hermaphroditic and can engage in both sexual and asexual reproduction
- Some have a single opening in the body, which serves as a mouth and an anus

MEMBERS INCLUDE
- Tapeworms
- Flukes

THE ANNELIDS

COMMON CHARACTERISTICS
- Segmented body

MEMBERS INCLUDE
- Marine polychaetes (about 9,000 species)
- Earthworms (more than 4,000 species)
- Leeches (about 500 species)

THE MOLLUSKS

COMMON CHARACTERISTICS
- Most have a shell that protects the soft body
- Mantle (tissue that forms the shell)
- Radula (sandpaper-like tongue structure used during feeding) Found in all mollusks except bivalves

MEMBERS INCLUDE
- Gastropods (about 35,000 species)
- Bivalves (about 8,000 species)
- Cephalopods (about 600 species)

THE ROUNDWORMS

COMMON CHARACTERISTICS
- Long, narrow unsegmented body
- Bilaterally symmetrical
- Surrounded by a strong, flexible cuticle
- Must molt in order to grow larger

MEMBERS INCLUDE
- More than 90,000 species (but there may be five times as many species that have not yet been identified)

THE ARTHROPODS

COMMON CHARACTERISTICS
- Segmented body with a distinct head, thorax, and abdomen
- Exoskeleton made of chitin
- Jointed appendages

MEMBERS INCLUDE
- Insects (more than 800,000 species)
- Arachnids (about 60,000 species)
- Crustaceans (about 52,000 species)
- Millipedes and centipedes (about 10,000 species)

THE ECHINODERMS

COMMON CHARACTERISTICS
- Enclosed by a hard skeleton under spiny skin
- Larvae are bilaterally symmetrical
- Adults are radially symmetrical
- Undersides are covered with tube feet that aid in locomotion and grasping

MEMBERS INCLUDE
- Sea stars (about 1,600 species)
- Sea urchins and sand dollars (about 940 species)
- Sea cucumbers (about 1,100 species)

What Is LIFE? SECOND EDITION A GUIDE TO BIOLOGY **Jay Phelan**

10·7–10·9 Evolutionary trees help us conceptualize and categorize biodiversity.

Evolutionary trees reveal the evolutionary history of species and the sequence of speciation events that gave rise to them.

THE EVOLUTIONARY TREE OF LIFE

The evolutionary tree of life has branches with millions of tips representing all species on earth. As speciation events occur, new branches are added to the tree.

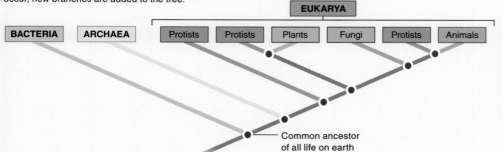

Common ancestor of all life on earth

MONOPHYLETIC GROUPS

Members of a monophyletic group share a common ancestor, and the group contains all of the descendants of that ancestor.

CONSTRUCTING EVOLUTIONARY TREES

Evolutionary trees are best constructed by comparing DNA sequences among organisms rather than comparing physical similarities, because convergent evolution can cause distantly related organisms to appear closely related, but it doesn't increase their DNA sequence similarity.

10·10–10·13 Macroevolution gives rise to great diversity.

The process of evolution in conjunction with reproductive isolation is sufficient to produce speciation and the rich diversity of life on earth.

EVOLUTION: MICRO VS. MACRO

Evolution is one thing only: a change in allele frequencies within a population. But over time, these changes can lead to new species and groups of species that vary tremendously.

MACROEVOLUTION

The accumulated effect of microevolution over a long period of time

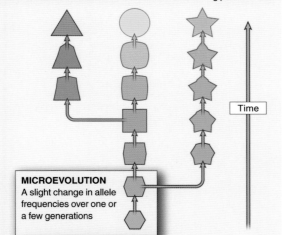

Time

MICROEVOLUTION
A slight change in allele frequencies over one or a few generations

THE TEMPO OF EVOLUTION

The pace of evolution varies for different species. Some species have evolved gradually over time, while others spend vast amounts of time with little change.

GRADUAL CHANGE

Evolution by creeps: The pace of evolution occurs gradually in incremental steps.

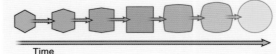

Time

PUNCTUATED EQUILIBRIUM

Evolution by jerks: Long periods of relatively little evolutionary change are punctuated by bursts of rapid change.

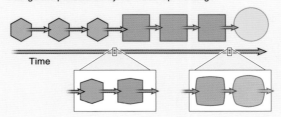

Time

ADAPTIVE RADIATION

Adaptive radiations—brief periods of time during which a small number of species diversify into a much larger number of species—tend to be triggered by mass extinctions of potentially competing species, colonizations of new habitats, or the appearance of evolutionary innovations.

EXTINCTION

Over time, species can be lost through extinction, which may be a consequence of natural selection or large, sudden changes in the environment. Mass extinctions are periods during which a large number of species on earth become extinct over a short period of time. These events are usually followed by periods of unusually rapid adaptive radiation and diversification of the remaining species.

10·14–10·17 An overview of the diversity of life on earth: organisms are divided into three domains.

All life on earth can be divided into three domains—bacteria, archaea, and eukarya—which reflect species' evolutionary relatedness to each other.

BACTERIA

All bacteria share a common ancestor and have a few features in common. They are prokaryotic, asexual, single-celled organisms with no nucleus or organelles, with one or more circular molecules of DNA as their genetic material, and using several methods of exchanging genetic information. Bacteria have a much broader diversity of metabolic and reproductive abilities than do the eukarya.

ARCHAEA

Archaea, many of which are adapted to life in extreme environments, physically resemble bacteria (because both domains include only prokaryotes) but are more closely related to eukarya.
Because they thrive in many habitats that humans have not yet studied well, including the deepest seas and oceans, they may turn out to be much more common than currently believed.

EUKARYA

All living organisms that we can see with the naked eye (and many that are too small to be seen) are eukarya, including all plants, animals, and fungi. The eukarya are unique among the three domains in having cells with organelles.

10·1–10·2 Life on earth most likely originated from non-living materials.

The earliest life on earth, which resembled bacteria, appeared about 3.5 billion years ago, not long after the earth was formed.

WHAT IS LIFE?

Life is defined by the ability to replicate and by the presence of some sort of metabolic activity (the chemical processes by which molecules are acquired and used and energy is transformed in controlled reactions).

THE UREY-MILLER EXPERIMENT

In 1953, Stanley Miller and Harold Urey developed a simple four-step experiment that demonstrated how complex organic molecules could have arisen in earth's early environment.

1 They created a model of the "warm little pond" and atmosphere early in the earth's history.

2 The atmosphere was subjected to sparks, to simulate lightning.

3 The atmosphere was cooled so that any compounds in it would rain back down into the water.

4 They examined the water, looking for organic molecules.

Electrical discharge

Heat

Cool

THE ORIGIN OF LIFE?

How did the first organisms on earth arise? Most scientists believe that life originated on earth, probably in several distinct phases.

FORMATION OF SMALL MOLECULES CONTAINING CARBON AND HYDROGEN
Because of carbon's chemical structure, it can form a huge variety of molecules with widely varying functions.

FORMATION OF SELF-REPLICATING, INFORMATION-CONTAINING MOLECULES
The nucleic acid RNA can both carry information and catalyze the reactions necessary for replication. Thus, this single molecule could have been a self-replicating system and precursor to cellular life.

DEVELOPMENT OF A MEMBRANE
Membranes that compartmentalized the self-replicating molecules from their surroundings would have facilitated metabolic activity.

10·3–10·6 Species are the basic units of biodiversity.

Species are distinct biological entities, named using a hierarchical system of classification.

WHAT IS A SPECIES?

According to the biological species concept, species are populations of organisms that interbreed, or could possibly interbreed, with each other under natural conditions, and that cannot interbreed with organisms from other such groups.

REPRODUCTIVE ISOLATION

Reproductive isolation is the inability of individuals from two populations to produce fertile offspring with each other, thereby making it impossible for gene exchange between the populations to occur.

SPECIATION

Speciation is the process by which one species splits into two distinct species that are reproductively isolated. It can occur by polyploidy or by a combination of reproductive isolation and genetic divergence.

THE ORGANIZATION OF LIFE

Each species on earth, like *Equus quagga*, is given a scientific name and is categorized according to hierarchical groups.

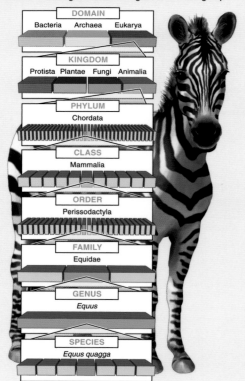

DOMAIN — Bacteria, Archaea, Eukarya
KINGDOM — Protista, Plantae, Fungi, Animalia
PHYLUM — Chordata
CLASS — Mammalia
ORDER — Perissodactyla
FAMILY — Equidae
GENUS — *Equus*
SPECIES — *Equus quagga*

THE BIOLOGICAL SPECIES CONCEPT DOESN'T ALWAYS WORK

The biological species concept is very useful when describing most plants and animals, but it doesn't work for distinguishing all life forms.

CLASSIFYING ASEXUAL SPECIES
Asexual reproduction does not involve interbreeding, so the concept of reproductive isolation is no longer meaningful.

CLASSIFYING FOSSIL SPECIES
Differences in size and shape of fossil bones cannot reveal whether there was reproductive isolation between the individuals from which the bones came.

DETERMINING WHEN ONE SPECIES HAS CHANGED INTO ANOTHER
Often, there is not a definitive moment marking the transition from one species to another.

CLASSIFYING RING SPECIES
Two non-interbreeding populations may be connected to each other through another population, so there is no exact point where one species stops and the other begins.

CLASSIFYING HYBRIDIZING SPECIES
Hybridization sometimes occurs and produces fertile offspring, suggesting that the borders between the species are not always clear cut.

What Is LIFE? SECOND EDITION   A GUIDE TO BIOLOGY   Jay Phelan

9·10–9·15 Sexual conflict can result from disparities in reproductive investment by males and females.

There are differences between males and females in the patterns of investment in reproduction.

DIFFERENCES IN MALE AND FEMALE REPRODUCTIVE BEHAVIORS

In mammals and many other animals, there are important physical differences between males and females relating to reproduction. These differences have led to the evolution of differences in male and female reproductive behaviors.

Males tend to increase their reproductive success by mating with many females and have evolved to compete among themselves to get the opportunity to mate. Females do not increase their reproductive success through extra matings, but rather by caring for their offspring and being choosy when selecting a mate.

FACTORS IN MATE SELECTION

Female choosiness (and the male-male competition it leads to) tends to increase the likelihood that a female will select only those males that have plentiful resources or relatively high-quality genes. Female choosiness is manifested by four general rules.

COURTSHIP RITUALS
A female grebe requires the male to perform a courtship dance before she will mate with him.

GIFTS UP FRONT
A female hanging fly will not mate with a male unless he brings her a large offering of food.

CONTROL OF VALUABLE RESOURCES
Female yellow-bellied marmots prefer rock outcroppings that provide retreats for predator escape and for hibernation (and are controlled by dominant males).

GOOD LOOKS
A female peacock is attracted to a male with the most beautiful tail feathers.

MATE GUARDING

Mate guarding reduces additional mating opportunities for a partner and can improve a male's reproductive success by increasing his paternity certainty, reducing his vulnerability when investing in offspring.

MATING SYSTEMS

Mating systems describe the variation in number of mates and the reproductive success of males and females. They are influenced by the relative amounts of males' and females' parental investment.

POLYGAMOUS MATING SYSTEMS
Some individuals attract multiple mates while other individuals attract none. Polygamous mating systems can be subdivided into polygyny, in which individual males mate with multiple females (such as in elephant seals), and polyandry, in which individual females mate with multiple males.

MONOGAMOUS MATING SYSTEMS
Individuals mate and remain with just one other individual.

SEXUAL DIMORPHISM AND MONOMORPHISM

Differences in the level of competition among individuals of each sex for access to mating opportunities can lead to the evolution of male-female differences in body size and other aspects of appearance.

SEXUAL DIMORPHISM
• The sexes differ in size or appearance.
• One parent invests more in caring for the offspring.
• Mating system tends toward polygamy.
• One sex (usually males) competes for access to mating opportunities with the other sex.

SEXUAL MONOMORPHISM
• The sexes are indistinguishable.
• Both parents invest (approximately) equally in caring for the offspring.
• Mating system tends toward monogamy.

9·16–9·17 Communication and the design of signals evolve.

The challenge of communication is central to the evolution of animal behaviors.

FORMS OF ANIMAL COMMUNICATION

Methods of communication have evolved in animal species, enabling individuals to convey information about their condition and situation. These abilities influence fitness and the evolution of almost all other behaviors.

CHEMICAL COMMUNICATION
Pheromones released by one individual and detected by another using its antennae, can trigger behavioral responses.

AUDITORY COMMUNICATION
Sounds, such as the howl of a coyote, are a common method of triggering behavior responses.

VISUAL COMMUNICATION
Organisms can convey information, such as threat or receptivity, with visual displays. Here, a balloonfish puffs up its body in response to a predator.

9 EVOLUTION and BEHAVIOR...*to go*

As long as they satisfy the three necessary conditions for natural selection (variation, heritability, and differential reproductive success), behaviors can evolve just as physical traits can.

BEHAVIOR

Behavior encompasses any and all of the actions performed by an organism. Behavior is as much a part of an organism's phenotype as is an anatomical structure, and as such it can be produced and shaped by natural selection.

INNATE BEHAVIORS

Innate behaviors are present in all individuals in a population and do not vary much from one individual to another or over an individual's life span.

In geese, the sight of an egg outside the nest triggers a fixed action pattern: the goose uses a side-to-side egg-retrieval movement all the way back to the nest, even if the egg is taken away during the process.

The bellies of male stickleback fish turn bright red when the breeding season arrives. During this time, a male stickleback reacts aggressively to the sight of a red belly on any other male stickleback.

LEARNED BEHAVIORS

Learned behaviors are those behaviors that are influenced more by the individual's environment, requiring some learning, and are often altered and modified over time in response to past experiences. Organisms are well-prepared to learn behaviors that have been important to the reproductive success of their ancestors, and less prepared to learn behaviors irrelevant to their evolutionary success. For example, a monkey quickly learns to fear snakes if it sees another monkey express such fear.

1 BEFORE EXPOSURE TO FEAR OF SNAKES
A captive monkey will reach over a plastic snake for food.

2 EXPOSURE TO FEAR OF SNAKES
A captive monkey views another monkey expressing fear at the sight of a snake.

3 AFTER EXPOSURE TO FEAR OF SNAKES
A captive monkey expresses fear of the plastic snake.

COMPLEX-APPEARING BEHAVIORS

Complex-appearing behaviors don't necessarily require complex thought to evolve. The natural selection of such behaviors does not require the organism to consciously try to maximize its reproductive success.

Many behaviors in the animal world that *appear* to be altruistic behaviors can be explained.

APPARENT ALTRUISM

Many behaviors in the animal world appear altruistic. In almost all cases, such acts are not truly altruistic and have evolved as a consequence of kin selection or reciprocal altruism, and from an evolutionary perspective are beneficial to the individual engaging in the behavior.

KIN SELECTION

Kin selection describes apparently altruistic behavior in which an individual that assists a genetic relative compensates for its own decrease in direct fitness by helping increase the relative's fitness and, consequently, its own inclusive fitness.

At great risk to herself, a female Belding's ground squirrel will make an alarm in response to a predator, which is likely to save individuals with whom she is related. Because she protects her genetic relatives, the alarm-calling behavior is favored by natural selection.

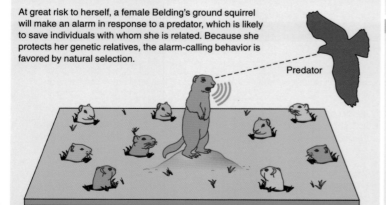

Predator

LEARNED BEHAVIOR

Reciprocal altruism describes altruistic-appearing acts in which the individual performing the act is likely to get something of value from the recipient at a later time. The evolution of reciprocal altruism requires that individuals have repeated interactions and can recognize and punish cheaters, conditions satisfied in humans but in few other species.

A vampire bat may vomit up a blood meal for an unrelated individual—saving that individual's life. Bats preferentially do this for individuals that have done so for them previously (and will return the favor), improving their own survival in the long run.

GROUP SELECTION

Group selection describes the evolution of a trait that is beneficial for the species or population while decreasing the fitness of the individual exhibiting the trait. Behaviors that are good for the species or population but detrimental to the individual exhibiting such behaviors are not generally produced in a population under natural conditions.

ALLELE FREQUENCIES

- proportion of **selfless behavior** allele in the population ("do what's best for the group, even though it reduces your own reproductive output")
- proportion of **selfish behavior** allele in the population ("do what's best for you, even if it hurts the group")

Time

8·12–8·17 Through natural selection, populations of organisms can become adapted to their environments.

When there is variation for a trait, and the variation is heritable, and there is differential reproductive success based on that trait, evolution by natural selection is occurring.

FITNESS

Fitness is a measure of the relative amount of reproduction of an individual with a particular phenotype, as compared with the reproductive output of individuals with alternative phenotypes. An individual's fitness can vary, depending on the environment in which the individual lives.

In a lighter habitat, the allele for light-colored fur is fitter and increases in frequency:

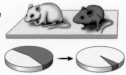

Frequency of alleles for light-colored fur and dark-colored fur

In a darker habitat, the allele for dark-colored fur is fitter and increases in frequency:

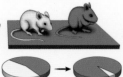

Frequency of alleles for light-colored fur and dark-colored fur

ADAPTATION

Adaptation—the process by which the organisms in a population become better matched to their environment and the specific features that make an organism more fit—occurs as a result of natural selection.

However, adaptation does not lead to perfect organisms. For example, the average beak size in Galápagos finches fluctuates according to average rainfall and food supply.

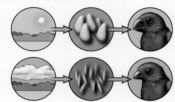

PATTERNS OF NATURAL SELECTION

Natural selection can change populations in several ways.

DIRECTIONAL SELECTION
The average value for the trait increases or decreases.

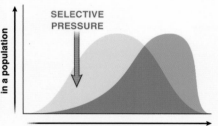

Proportion of individuals in a population / SELECTIVE PRESSURE / Average value for a trait

STABILIZING SELECTION
The average value of a trait remains the same while extreme versions of the trait are selected against.

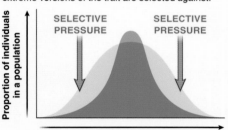

Proportion of individuals in a population / SELECTIVE PRESSURE / SELECTIVE PRESSURE / Average value for a trait

DISRUPTIVE SELECTION
Individuals with extreme phenotypes have the highest fitness.

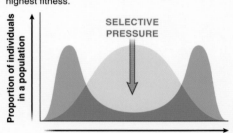

Proportion of individuals in a population / SELECTIVE PRESSURE / Average value for a trait

8·18–8·22 The evidence for evolution is overwhelming.

Many overwhelming lines of evidence document the occurrence of evolution and point to the central and unifying role of evolution by natural selection in helping us to better understand all other ideas and facts in biology.

THE FOSSIL RECORD

Analysis of fossil remains enables biologists to reconstruct what organisms looked like long ago, learn how organisms were related to each other, and understand how groups of organisms evolved over time.

Lobe-finned fish   *Tiktaalik*   Early amphibian

BIOGEOGRAPHY

Observing geographic patterns of species distributions helps us to understand the evolutionary histories of populations. For example, Hawaiian honeycreepers have adapted to a wide range of habitats, yet still closely resemble a finch-like shared ancestor found nearly 2,000 miles away.

COMPARATIVE ANATOMY AND EMBRYOLOGY

Similarities in the anatomy and development of different groups of organisms and in their physical appearance can reveal common evolutionary origins.

■ Gill pouches   ■ Bony tail

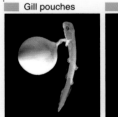

Shark embryo

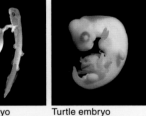

Turtle embryo

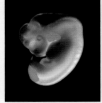

Human embryo

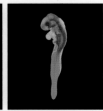

Chicken embryo

COMMON GENETIC SEQUENCES

All living organisms share the same genetic code. The degree of similarity in the DNA sequences of different species can reveal how closely related they are and the amount of time that has passed since they last shared a common ancestor.

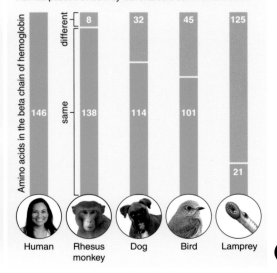

Amino acids in the beta chain of hemoglobin

different / same

	Human	Rhesus monkey	Dog	Bird	Lamprey
different		8	32	45	125
same	146	138	114	101	21

What Is LIFE? SECOND EDITION   A GUIDE TO BIOLOGY   Jay Phelan

8 EVOLUTION and NATURAL SELECTION...*to go*

8·1 Evolution is an ongoing process.

Characteristics of the individuals that make up a population can change over time. We can observe such change in nature and can even cause such change to occur.

EVOLUTION IN ACTION

In an experiment that tests how long fruit flies can survive without food, evolution occurs right before our eyes. In the experiment, only the fruit flies that survive the longest go on to reproduce and populate the next generation.

The average starvation resistance time is recorded for each generation. Over many generations of natural selection, the population changes. The fruit flies of generation 60 can survive without food much longer than the first generation.

GENERATION 1
Avg. starvation resistance:
20 HRS

GENERATION 2
Avg. starvation resistance:
23 HRS

GENERATION 60
Avg. starvation resistance:
160 HRS

Number of flies — Hours until starvation (0, 40, 80, 120, 160, 200)

8·2–8·5 Darwin journeyed to a new idea.

Charles Darwin developed a theory of evolution by natural selection that explained how populations of species can change over time.

DARWIN'S INFLUENCES

In the 18th and 19th centuries, gradual changes in scientists' beliefs helped shape Charles Darwin's thinking.

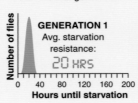 **GEORGES BUFFON** (1707–1788)
Suggested that the earth was much older than previously believed.

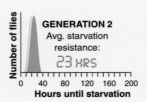 **GEORGES CUVIER** (1769–1832)
By documenting fossil discoveries, showed that extinction had occurred.

JEAN-BAPTISTE LAMARCK (1744–1829)
Suggested that living species might change over time.

CHARLES LYELL (1797–1875)
Argued that geological forces had gradually shaped the earth and continue to do so.

DARWIN'S OBSERVATIONS

Darwin noted unexpected patterns among living organisms he observed and fossils he discovered while on the voyage of the Beagle.

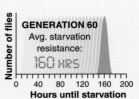 **FINCHES**
The 13 species of finches found on the Galápagos islands all had slightly different physical characteristics, but they still resembled the single mainland finch.

FOSSILS
Around the world, there is a striking similarity between the fossils of extinct species found in an area and the living species in that same area.

Glyptodont (extinct)   Armadillo

8·6–8·11 Four mechanisms can give rise to evolution.

Evolution—a change in the allele frequencies in a population—can occur via mutation, genetic drift, migration, or natural selection.

MUTATION

Mutation is an alteration of the base-pair sequence in an individual's DNA. Such an alteration constitutes evolution if it changes an allele that the individual carries.

Mutated base-pair sequence

Mutated protein

MIGRATION

Migration, or gene flow, leads to a change in allele frequencies in a population as individuals move into or out of the population.

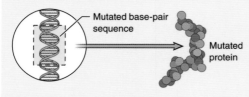

Population 1   Population 2

GENETIC DRIFT

Genetic drift is a random change in allele frequencies within a population, unrelated to the alleles' influence on reproductive success.

Population before genetic drift

Population after genetic drift

Two special cases of genetic drift:

 FOUNDER EFFECT
The founding members of a new population can have different allele frequencies than the original source population.

 BOTTLENECK EFFECT
The surviving members of a catastrophic event can have different allele frequencies than the source population.

NATURAL SELECTION

Natural selection is a mechanism of evolution that occurs when the following three conditions are satisfied:

VARIATION FOR A TRAIT
Different traits are present in individuals of the same species.

HERITABILITY
Traits are passed on from parents to their children.

DIFFERENTIAL REPRODUCTIVE SUCCESS
In a population, individuals with traits most suited to reproduction in their environment generally leave more offspring than individuals with alternative traits.

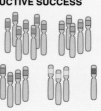

 **What Is LIFE?** A GUIDE TO BIOLOGY **Jay Phelan**

7·9–7·14 The translation of genotypes into phenotypes is not a black box.

The world in which each trait is coded for by a single gene with two alleles—one completely dominant and one recessive—and with no environmental effects at all doesn't quite capture the complexity of the world beyond Mendel's pea plants.

INCOMPLETE DOMINANCE

Sometimes the effects of both alleles in a heterozygous genotype are evident in the phenotype. With incomplete dominance, the phenotype of a heterozygote appears to be an intermediate blend of the phenotypes of the two homozygotes. For example, when true-breeding white and red snapdragons are crossed, offspring have pink flowers.

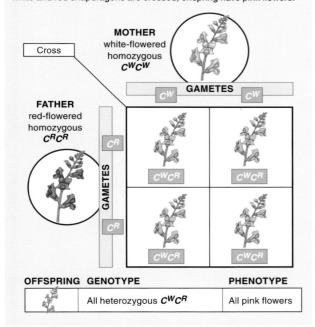

Cross

MOTHER
white-flowered homozygous
C^WC^W

GAMETES C^W C^W

FATHER
red-flowered homozygous
C^RC^R

GAMETES C^R C^R

C^WC^R C^WC^R
C^WC^R C^WC^R

OFFSPRING	GENOTYPE	PHENOTYPE
	All heterozygous C^WC^R	All pink flowers

CODOMINANCE

In codominance, neither allele masks the effect of the other and the heterozygote displays characteristics of both homozygotes. For example, when white chickens are crossed with black chickens, the offspring all have both white and black feathers.

MULTIPLE ALLELISM

Multiple allelism occurs when there are three or more alleles for a gene within a population. An individual still inherits only two alleles—one from each parent. For example, red blood cells have 6 different genotypes (**AA**, **AO**, **BB**, **BO**, **AB**, and **OO**). These genotypes result in 4 different phenotypes (type A, type B, type AB, and type O).

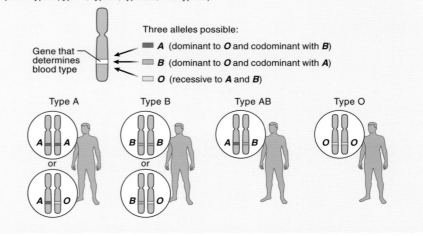

Gene that determines blood type

Three alleles possible:
- **A** (dominant to **O** and codominant with **B**)
- **B** (dominant to **O** and codominant with **A**)
- **O** (recessive to **A** and **B**)

Type A   Type B   Type AB   Type O
A A B B A B O O
or   or
A O B O

PLEIOTROPY

Pleiotropy occurs when one gene influences multiple, unrelated traits. The allele for sickle-cell disease is pleiotropic: it causes red blood cells to form an unusual, sickled shape, and it also provides resistance to malaria.

Hb^AHb^A HOMOZYGOTE
- Does not have sickle-cell disease
- Is susceptible to malaria

Hb^SHb^A HETEROZYGOTE
- Does not have sickle-cell disease
- Is immune to malaria

Hb^SHb^S HOMOZYGOTE
- Has sickle-cell disease
- Is immune to malaria

POLYGENIC TRAITS

Many traits, including continuously varying traits such as height, eye color, and skin color, are influenced by multiple genes.

SEX-LINKED TRAITS

The patterns of inheritance of most traits do not differ between males and females. However, when a trait is coded for by a gene on a sex chromosome, such as color vision on the X chromosome, the pattern of expression differs for males and females.

ENVIRONMENTAL FACTORS

Genotypes are not like blueprints that specify phenotypes. Rather, phenotypes are a product of the genotype in combination with the environment.

7·15–7·16 Some genes are linked together.

Most traits are passed on as independent features, however, alleles that are closely linked on the same chromosome can be passed on to offspring in one bundle.

MENDEL'S LAW OF INDEPENDENT ASSORTMENT

Genes tend to behave independently, such that the inheritance pattern of one trait doesn't usually influence the inheritance of any other trait.

MOTHER and FATHER
pigmented heterozygous **Aa**
dimpled chin heterozygous **Dd**

IF...
Parents are both heterozygous for both traits (i.e., "doubly heterozygous"). Four different types of gametes are produced by each: **AD**, **Ad**, **aD**, and **ad**.

THEN...
The genotype proportions for **A/a** are still ¼ **AA**, ½ **Aa**, and ¼ **aa**. And the genotype proportions for **D/d** are still ¼ **DD**, ½ **Dd**, and ¼ **dd**.

LINKED GENES

When genes are located close together on the same chromosome, the alleles for genes are inherited and expressed almost as a package deal.

Linked genes

Maternal copy   Paternal copy

When crossing over occurs, linked genes usually stay together.

Chromatids after the exchange of genetic information

What Is LIFE? SECOND EDITION   A GUIDE TO BIOLOGY   **Jay Phelan**

7·1–7·5 Why do offspring resemble their parents?

Offspring inherit genes—instruction sets for biochemical, physical, and behavioral traits, some of which are responsible for diseases—from their parents.

GREGOR MENDEL

In the mid-1800s, Gregor Mendel conducted studies that help us understand heredity. He focused on easily observed and categorized traits in garden peas and applied methodical experimentation and rigorous hypothesis testing to determine how traits are inherited.

MENDEL'S LAW OF SEGREGATION

According to Mendel's law of segregation, each parent puts a single set of instructions for building a particular trait into every sperm or egg it makes. This instruction set is called a gene. The trait observed in an individual depends on the two copies (alleles) of the gene it inherits from its parents.

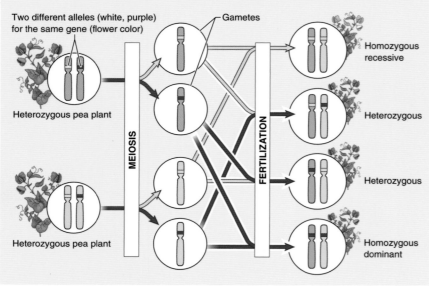

USING PUNNETT SQUARES TO DETERMINE GENOTYPES

It is not always possible to determine an individual's genetic makeup, known as its genotype, by observation of the organism's outward appearance, known as its phenotype. For a particular trait, an individual may carry a recessive allele whose phenotypic effect is masked by the presence of a dominant allele. We can trace the possible outcomes of a cross between 2 individuals using a tool called a Punnett Square.

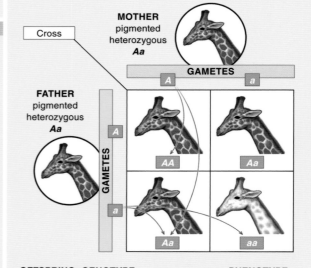

OFFSPRING	GENOTYPE	PHENOTYPE
	1/4 homozygous dominant **AA**	3/4 pigmented
	2/4 heterozygous **Aa**	
	1/4 homozygous recessive **aa**	1/4 albino

7·6–7·8 Probability and chance play central roles in genetics.

Sometimes genetics is a bit like gambling. Even with perfect information, it can still be impossible to know the genetic outcome with certainty.

GENETICS AND PROBABILITY

It is possible to determine the probability of a complex genetic event occurring if you know the probability of each component. You multiply all the probabilities together to get the overall probability of the event.

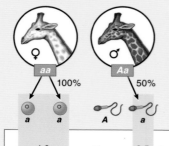

IF...
The mother is albino, and the father is heterozygous.

THEN...
There is a 100% chance that the mother's egg will carry the recessive *a* allele and a 50% chance that a sperm will carry the recessive *a* allele.

| 1.0 | × | 0.5 | = 0.5 or 50% chance the offspring will be albino. |

AND...

Multiply the two components together to determine the overall probability.

PEDIGREES

Pedigrees help scientists, doctors, animal and plant breeders, and prospective parents determine the genes that individuals carry and the likelihood that the offspring of two individuals will exhibit a given trait.

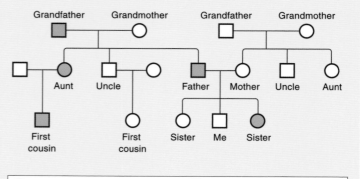

- ● Female exhibiting trait of interest
- ○ Female not exhibiting trait
- ■ Male exhibiting trait of interest
- □ Male not exhibiting trait

6·10 – 6·14 Meiosis generates sperm and eggs and a great deal of variation.

Meiosis occurs only in gamete-producing cells of sexually reproducing organisms.

SEXUAL REPRODUCTION

Diploid organisms produce haploid gametes that fuse at fertilization and return to the diploid state.

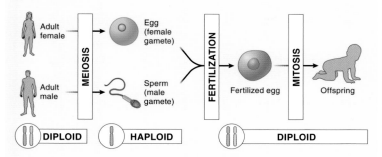

SOURCES OF GENETIC VARIATION

There are multiple reasons why offspring are genetically different from their parents and one another.

ALLELES COME FROM TWO PARENTS
Each parent donates his or her own set of genetic material (a copy of one of the alleles they carry for each gene).

CROSSING OVER
During gamete production, crossing over during meiosis produces a mixture of maternal and paternal genetic material on each chromatid.

REASSORTMENT OF HOMOLOGUES
During gamete production, the homologues and sister chromatids distributed to each daughter cell during meiosis are a random mix of their maternal and paternal genetic material.

MEIOSIS

Meiosis consists of two rounds of cell division: separation of homologous pairs of sister chromatids, then separation of the sister chromatids. The final product are haploid gametes.

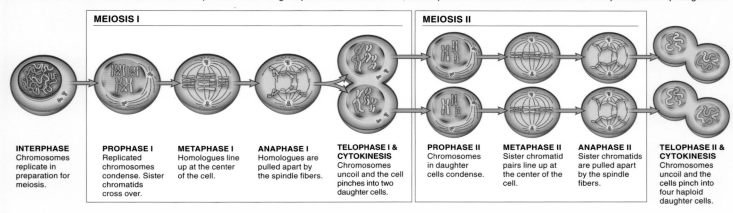

MEIOSIS I

MEIOSIS II

INTERPHASE
Chromosomes replicate in preparation for meiosis.

PROPHASE I
Replicated chromosomes condense. Sister chromatids cross over.

METAPHASE I
Homologues line up at the center of the cell.

ANAPHASE I
Homologues are pulled apart by the spindle fibers.

TELOPHASE I & CYTOKINESIS
Chromosomes uncoil and the cell pinches into two daughter cells.

PROPHASE II
Chromosomes in daughter cells condense.

METAPHASE II
Sister chromatid pairs line up at the center of the cell.

ANAPHASE II
Sister chromatids are pulled apart by the spindle fibers.

TELOPHASE II & CYTOKINESIS
Chromosomes uncoil and the cells pinch into four haploid daughter cells.

6·15 – 6·16 There are sex differences in the chromosomes.

Sex chromosomes carry information that directs a growing fetus to develop as a male or as a female.

SEX DETERMINATION IN HUMANS

When the sperm carries an X, the baby will have two X chromosomes and develop as female.

When the sperm carries a Y, the baby will have an X and a Y and develop as male.

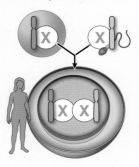

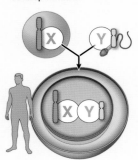

6·17 – 6·18 Deviations from the normal chromosome number lead to problems.

An error during meiosis can produce gametes with too many or too few chromosomes, usually leading to serious consequences for health.

NONDISJUNCTION

Nondisjunction is the unequal distribution of chromosomes during meiosis. The resulting gametes have zero or two copies of a chromosome, rather than a single copy.

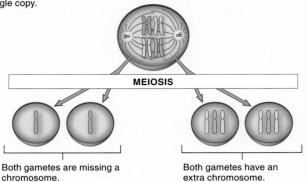

MEIOSIS

Both gametes are missing a chromosome.

Both gametes have an extra chromosome.

What Is LIFE? SECOND EDITION **A GUIDE TO BIOLOGY** **Jay Phelan**

6·1– 6·5 There are different types of cell division.

Cell division is an ongoing process in most organisms and their tissues; disruptions to normal cell division can have serious consequences.

PROKARYOTIC AND EUKARYOTIC CHROMOSOMES

In most bacteria and archaea, the genetic information is carried in a single, circular chromosome, a strand of DNA that is attached at one site to the cell membrane. Eukaryotes have much more DNA than do bacteria and organize it into free-floating linear chromosomes within the nucleus.

PROKARYOTIC CELL   **EUKARYOTIC CELL**

Chromosomes

PROKARYOTIC CELL DIVISION: BINARY FISSION

Bacteria divide by a type of asexual reproduction called binary fission: first, the circular chromosome duplicates itself, then the parent cell splits into two new, genetically identical daughter cells.

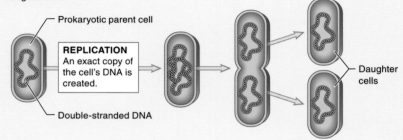

Prokaryotic parent cell

REPLICATION
An exact copy of the cell's DNA is created.

Double-stranded DNA

Daughter cells

EUKARYOTIC CELL CYCLE

Eukaryotic cells alternate in a cycle between cell division and other cell activities. In somatic cells, the cell division portion of the cycle is called the mitotic phase (M phase). The remainder of the cell cycle, called interphase, consists of two gap phases (during which cell growth and other metabolic activities occur) separated by a DNA synthesis phase during which the genetic material is replicated.

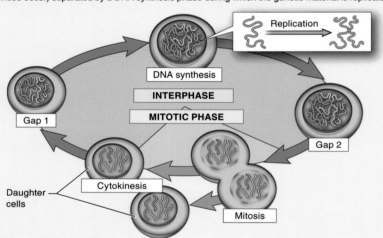

Replication

DNA synthesis

INTERPHASE

MITOTIC PHASE

Gap 1

Gap 2

Daughter cells

Cytokinesis

Mitosis

DNA REPLICATION

Every time a cell divides, its DNA must first duplicate so that each of the two new cells has all the genetic material of the parent cell.

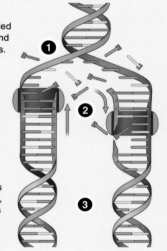

1 UNWINDING
The coiled, double-stranded DNA molecule unwinds and separates into two strands.

2 REBUILDING
Enzymes connect a nucleotide with the appropriate base to the growing new strand, as the base bonds with the exposed, complementary base.

3 Each of the single strands becomes a double strand, each identical to the cell's original double-stranded DNA molecule.

6·6– 6·9 Mitosis replaces worn-out old cells with fresh new duplicates.

In mitosis, cells generate new, genetically identical cells, enabling organisms to grow and replace cells.

MITOSIS

Mitosis occurs in four steps, following replication of the chromosomes, to produce two genetically identical daughter cells from one parent cell.

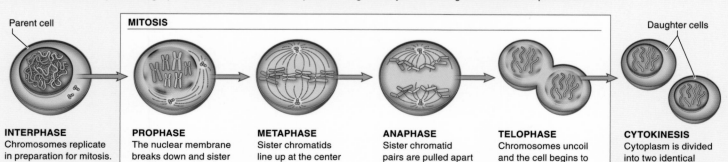

Parent cell

MITOSIS

Daughter cells

INTERPHASE
Chromosomes replicate in preparation for mitosis.

PROPHASE
The nuclear membrane breaks down and sister chromatids condense.

METAPHASE
Sister chromatids line up at the center of the cell.

ANAPHASE
Sister chromatid pairs are pulled apart by the spindle fibers.

TELOPHASE
Chromosomes uncoil and the cell begins to pinch in two.

CYTOKINESIS
Cytoplasm is divided into two identical daughter cells.

What Is LIFE? SECOND EDITION   A GUIDE TO **BIOLOGY**   **Jay Phelan**

5·9–5·10 Damage to the genetic code has a variety of causes and effects.

Mutations are alterations to the sequence of bases in an organism's DNA, and can lead to changes in the structure and function of the proteins produced.

MUTATIONS CAN HAVE A RANGE OF EFFECTS

Mutations are rare, but when they do occur, they may disrupt normal functioning of the body (although many mutations are neutral). Extremely rarely, mutations may have a beneficial effect. Mutations play an important role in evolution.

Normal fruit fly   Mutant fruit fly

TYPES OF MUTATIONS

Mutations generally fall into two types: point mutations and chromosomal aberrations.

POINT MUTATIONS
One base pair is changed. A base pair in the DNA can be substituted for another, or a base pair can be inserted or deleted.

CHROMOSOMAL ABERRATIONS
Entire sections of a chromosome are altered. Aberrations can involve the complete deletion of an entire section of DNA, the relocation of a gene, or the duplication of a gene.

5·11–5·13 Biotechnology is producing improvements in agriculture.

Biotechnology is the use of technology to modify organisms, cells, and their molecules to achieve practical benefits.

FIVE IMPORTANT TOOLS AND TECHNIQUES OF MOST BIOTECHNOLOGY PROCEDURES

With modern molecular methods, researchers can cut and copy DNA and deliver it to new organisms, not necessarily of the same species.

CHOP
Restriction enzymes are used to isolate a gene from a donor species that exhibits a trait of interest.

AMPLIFY
The polymerase chain reaction can duplicate a small strand of DNA into more useful quantities.

INSERT
Plasmids can be used to transfer DNA from one species to another.

GROW
A gene library (or clone library) is a collection of cloned DNA fragments.

IDENTIFY
A DNA probe is used to locate the desired clone in a gene library.

THE BENEFITS OF BIOTECHNOLOGY

Biotechnology has led to important advances in agriculture by using transgenic plants and animals to produce more nutritious food. Biotechnology has also reduced the environmental and financial costs of producing food through the creation of herbicide-resistant and insect-resistant crops. The ecological and health risks of such widespread use of transgenic species are not fully understood and are potentially great.

FEARS AND RISKS ASSOCIATED WITH BIOTECHNOLOGY

More and more genetically modified foods are being created using modern methods of recombinant DNA technology. Numerous legitimate fears among the public remain, however, about the potentially catastrophic risks of these foods, given that their development relies on such new technology, and about the long-term financial advantages they offer.

5·14–5·17 Biotechnology has the potential for improving human health (and criminal justice).

Advances in biotechnology have led to some successes in treating diseases, automated methods for analyzing DNA sequences, and the potential benefits of cloning.

USING BIOTECHNOLOGY TO TREAT DISEASE

Biotechnology has had some successes in treating diseases, usually by producing medicines more efficiently and effectively than with traditional methods. For example, the human insulin that is used to treat diabetes is engineered through recombinant DNA technology. Additionally, many tools have been developed that enable us to identify individuals carrying disease-causing genes. These tools can help reduce the symptoms and incidence of diseases, but come with significant potential costs, particularly the risk of discrimination.

CLONING

Cloning—which describes the production of genetically identical cells, organisms, or DNA molecules of individuals—has potential benefits in medicine and agriculture (the cloning of animals can maintain desirable traits from generation to generation), but ethical questions linger.

DNA FINGERPRINTING

Comparisons of highly variable DNA regions can be used to identify tissue specimens and determine the individual from whom they came.

Forensic scientists analyze regions of DNA that contain short tandem repeats, or STRs—sequences of DNA that repeat over and over again.

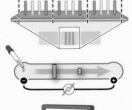

DNA fragments containing STRs are separated by size using electrophoresis.

Computer software is used to analyze the results. The number of repeats within an STR region is determined by comparing the length of the fragments containing that STR region to DNA fragments of known lengths.

4 ENERGY...*to go*

4·1– 4·4 Energy flows from the sun and through all life on earth.

Energy from the sun fuels all life on earth as it is converted to different forms.

ENERGY CAPTURE AND CONVERSION

Plants capture energy from the sun and store it in the chemical bonds of sugars and other food molecules. Organisms release the energy stored in the chemical bonds of food molecules they eat and use it as fuel.

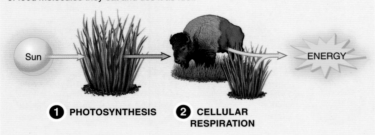

Sun → ❶ **PHOTOSYNTHESIS** → ❷ **CELLULAR RESPIRATION** → ENERGY

ENERGY TRANSFORMATIONS

As energy is captured and converted, the amount of energy available to do work decreases. Some energy is released as heat.

Light energy from the sun → Energy transformed into heat / Chemical energy stored in plants

KINETIC AND POTENTIAL ENERGY

Energy, the capacity to do work, comes in two forms.

KINETIC ENERGY | POTENTIAL ENERGY

KINETIC ENERGY
The energy of moving objects

POTENTIAL ENERGY
The energy that is stored in objects, including chemical bonds

ADENOSINE TRIPHOSPHATE (ATP) AND ADENOSINE DIPHOSPHATE (ADP)

Cells temporarily store energy in the bonds of ATP molecules. This potential energy can be converted to kinetic energy and used to fuel life-sustaining chemical reactions.

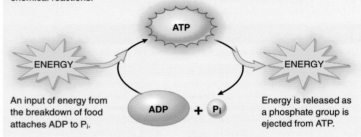

ATP
ENERGY
ADP + Pi
ENERGY

An input of energy from the breakdown of food attaches ADP to Pi.

Energy is released as a phosphate group is ejected from ATP.

4·5– 4·11 Photosynthesis uses energy from sunlight to make food. (continued on other side) ▶

In photosynthesis, plants transform light energy into the chemical energy of ATP and NADPH, while splitting water molecules and producing oxygen.

PHOTOSYNTHESIS: THE BIG PICTURE

Plants use water, the energy of sunlight, and carbon dioxide gas from the air to produce sugars and other organic materials. In the process, photosynthesizing organisms also produce oxygen, which makes all animal life possible.

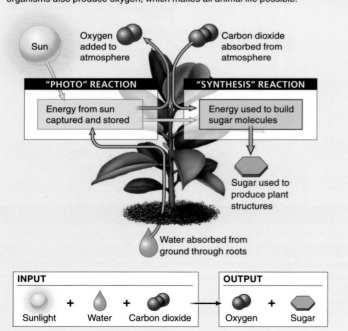

Sun / Oxygen added to atmosphere / Carbon dioxide absorbed from atmosphere

"PHOTO" REACTION | **"SYNTHESIS" REACTION**

Energy from sun captured and stored → Energy used to build sugar molecules

Sugar used to produce plant structures

Water absorbed from ground through roots

INPUT
Sunlight + Water + Carbon dioxide →

OUTPUT
Oxygen + Sugar

"PHOTO" REACTIONS

In the "photo" part of photosynthesis, chloroplasts transform light energy into the chemical energy of ATP and NADPH, while splitting water molecules and producing oxygen.

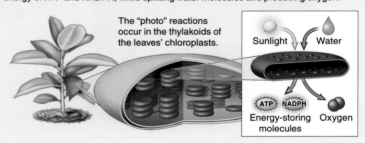

The "photo" reactions occur in the thylakoids of the leaves' chloroplasts.

Sunlight / Water

ATP NADPH
Energy-storing molecules

Oxygen

"SYNTHESIS" REACTIONS

In the Calvin cycle, the "synthesis" part of photosynthesis, carbon from CO_2 in the atmosphere is attached to molecules in chloroplasts to build sugars. This production of sugars consumes ATP and NADPH generated in the "photo" part of photosynthesis.

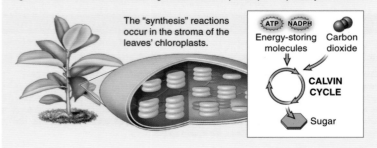

The "synthesis" reactions occur in the stroma of the leaves' chloroplasts.

ATP NADPH
Energy-storing molecules / Carbon dioxide

CALVIN CYCLE

Sugar

What Is LIFE? SECOND EDITION A GUIDE TO BIOLOGY **Jay Phelan**

3 CELLS...to go

3·12 Cells are connected and communicate with each other.

In multicellular organisms, most cells are connected to other cells by specialized structures that hold them in place and enable them to communicate with each other.

THREE DIFFERENT CONNECTIONS BETWEEN ANIMAL CELLS

TIGHT JUNCTIONS
Form a water-tight seal between cells, like caulking around a tub.

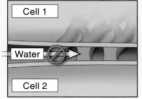

Cell 1
Water
Cell 2

DESMOSOMES
Act like velcro that holds sheets of cells together allowing fluid to pass between cells.

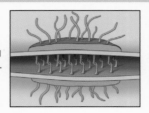

GAP JUNCTIONS
Function like secret passageways that allow materials to pass between cells.

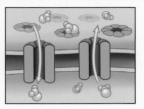

3·13–3·21 Nine important landmarks distinguish eukaryotic cells.

Specialized structures in cells perform specific life-sustaining functions.

NUCLEUS

The nucleus is the genetic control center of eukaryotic cells. It directs protein production and is the storehouse for all hereditary information.

Nucleolus
Pore
Nuclear membrane

CYTOSKELETON

The cytoskeleton is the inner scaffolding of a cell, giving it shape, support, and serving as a series of tracks on which organelles and molecules are guided around the inside of the cell.

Microtubules

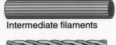

Intermediate filaments

Microfilaments

MITOCHONDRIA

Mitochondria are found in virtually all eukaryotic cells and act as all-purpose energy converters, harvesting energy to be used for cellular functions.

Outer membrane
Inner membrane
Matrix
Intermembrane space

LYSOSOMES

Lysosomes are acid-filled organelles that function as cellular garbage disposals.

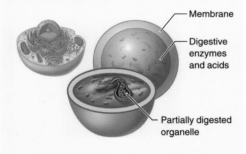

Membrane
Digestive enzymes and acids
Partially digested organelle

ENDOPLASMIC RETICULUM

The production and modification of biological molecules in eukaryotic cells occurs in a system of organelles called the endomembrane system, which includes the rough and smooth endoplasmic reticulum.

ROUGH ER
Folds and packages proteins to be shipped elsewhere in the body.

SMOOTH ER
Lipids are synthesized and alcohol, antibiotics, and other drugs are detoxified.

GOLGI APPARATUS

Another organelle in the endomembrane system, the golgi apparatus processes and packages molecules destined for use elsewhere in the body.

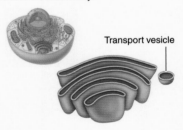

Transport vesicle

PLANT CELL WALL

The cell wall provides structural strength, increases resistance to water loss, and provides some protection from insects and other animals that might eat them.

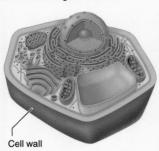

PLASMODESMATA
Connect cells to each other, enabling communication and transport between them.

Cell wall

VACUOLES

Vacuoles are storage spaces found in several eukaryotic taxa—and particularly prominent in plant cells—that play a role in nutrition, waste management, predator deterrence, reproduction, and physical support.

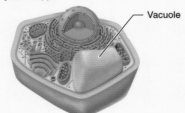

Vacuole

CHLOROPLASTS

The chloroplast is the organelle in plants and algae that is the site of photosynthesis—the conversion of light energy into chemical energy, with oxygen as a by-product.

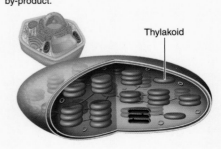

Thylakoid

What Is LIFE? A GUIDE TO BIOLOGY   Jay Phelan

3 CELLS...to go

The cell is the smallest unit of life that can perform all of the necessary activities of life. All living organisms are made up of one or more cells.

PROKARYOTIC CELLS

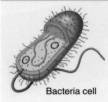

Bacteria cell

TYPICAL PROKARYOTIC CELL FEATURES
- No nucleus—circular DNA molecules are in the cytoplasm
- Internal structures not organized into compartments
- Much smaller than eukaryotes

EUKARYOTIC CELLS

Animal cell

Plant cell

TYPICAL EUKARYOTIC CELL FEATURES
- Linear DNA molecules are in nucleus
- Internal structures organized into compartments
- Larger than prokaryotes—usually at least 10 times bigger
- Cytoplasm contains specialized structures called organelles

3·4– 3·7 Cell membranes are gatekeepers.

Every cell is enclosed by a plasma membrane, a two-layered structure that holds the contents of a cell in place and regulates what enters and leaves the cell.

THE PLASMA MEMBRANE

The plasma membrane is a fluid mosaic of proteins, lipids and carbohydrates.

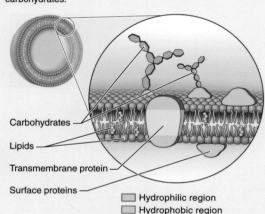

- Carbohydrates
- Lipids
- Transmembrane protein
- Surface proteins

☐ Hydrophilic region
☐ Hydrophobic region

FUNCTION OF PLASMA MEMBRANE MOLECULES

Plasma membrane molecules serve diverse roles.

RECEPTOR PROTEINS
Bind to external chemicals in order to regulate processes within the cell

RECOGNITION PROTEINS
Provide a "fingerprint" for the cell, so it can be recognized by other cells

TRANSPORT PROTEINS
Provide a passageway for molecules to travel into and out of the cell

ENZYMATIC PROTEINS
Accelerate intracellular and extracellular reactions on the plasma membrane

CARBOHYDRATE CHAINS
Provide a "fingerprint" for the cell, so it can be recognized by other cells

CHOLESTEROL
Helps the membrane retain its flexibility

3·8– 3·11 Molecules move across membranes in several ways.

Cells must import food molecules and other necessary materials from outside the cell and export metabolic waste and molecules produced for use elsewhere.

PASSIVE TRANSPORT

In passive transport the molecular movement occurs spontaneously, without the input of energy. This generally occurs as molecules move down their concentration gradient.

SIMPLE DIFFUSION
Molecules pass directly through the plasma membrane without the assistance of another molecule.

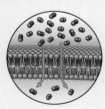

FACILITATED DIFFUSION
Molecules move across the plasma membrane with the help of a carrier molecule.

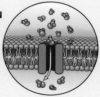

OSMOSIS
Water molecules diffuse across a membrane until the concentration of water inside and outside the cell is equalized.

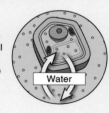
Water

ACTIVE TRANSPORT

Active transport is necessary if the molecules to be moved are very large or if they are being moved against their concentration gradient which requires energy in the form of ATP. Proteins embedded in the plasma membrane actively transport (pump) the molecules.

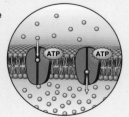
ATP ATP

ENDOCYTOSIS

The plasma membrane surrounds an object that is outside the cell, forming a little pocket called a vesicle.

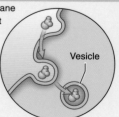
Vesicle

EXOCYTOSIS

A vesicle within a cell fuses with the cell's plasma membrane. Vesicle contents are released outside the cell.

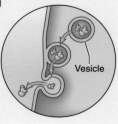
Vesicle

What Is LIFE? SECOND EDITION A GUIDE TO BIOLOGY
Jay Phelan

2·11–2·13 Lipids store energy for a rainy day.

Lipids are macromolecules—made up primarily from carbon, hydrogen, and oxygen—that are insoluble in water. Lipids are important for energy storage, hormones, and membrane structure. Their breakdown of dietary fats releases more energy per gram than other macromolecules.

FATS (TRIGLYCERIDES)

Lipids composed of a head region and three long tails. They provide long-term energy, storage, and insulation. When broken down they release significantly more energy per gram than other macromolecules.

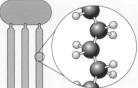

Head: Glycerol

Tails: Fatty acids

Energy is stored in the many hydrogen-carbon bonds of the tails.

STEROLS

Lipids composed of four interlinked rings of carbon atoms. They are important regulators of growth and development.

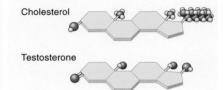

Cholesterol

Testosterone

PHOSPHOLIPIDS

The major component of cell membranes that surrounds the contents of a cell and controls the flow of chemicals into and out of the cell.

Hydrophilic head (attracted to water)

Hydrophobic tails (not attracted to water)

2·14–2·18 Proteins are versatile macromolecules that serve as building blocks.

Cells and tissues are primarily built from proteins, sequences of amino acids that fold into complex three-dimensional shapes. The atoms, especially nitrogen, present in the plant and animal proteins that an organism eats are essential to the organism's growth and repair.

PROTEIN STRUCTURE

The amino acid sequence of a protein determines how it folds into a particular three-dimensional shape. This shape determines many of the protein's features, such as which molecules it will interact with.

PRIMARY STRUCTURE
The sequence of amino acids in a polypeptide chain, similar to the sequence of letters that spell out a specific word

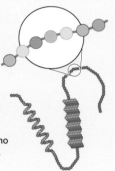

SECONDARY STRUCTURE
The corkscrew-like twists or pleated folds formed by hydrogen bonds between amino acids in the polypeptide chain.

TERTIARY STRUCTURE
The complex three-dimensional shape formed by multiple twists and bends in the polypeptide chain based on interactions between the side chains.

QUATERNARY STRUCTURE
Two or more polypeptide chains bonded together.

ENZYMES

Enzymes are proteins that help initiate and speed up chemical reactions. They aren't permanently altered in the process, but rather can be used again and again.

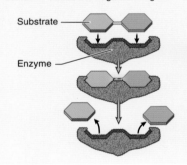

Substrate

Enzyme

2·19–2·21 Nucleic acids store information on how to build and run a body.

The nucleic acids DNA and RNA are macromolecules that store information by having unique sequences of molecules. Both play central roles in directing protein production in organisms. RNA acts as a universal translator of the genetic code into proteins. It reads DNA sequences and directs the production of a sequence of amino acids.

DEOXYRIBONUCLEIC ACID (DNA)

Two sugar-phosphate backbones spiral around each other, forming a double helix. The backbones are connected to each other by nucleotide base pairs. The sequence of nucleotides contains the information about how to produce a particular protein.

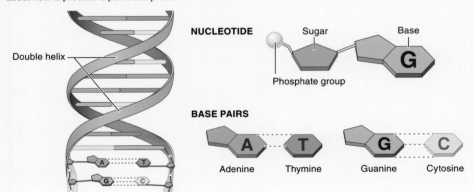

Double helix

NUCLEOTIDE

Sugar

Base

G

Phosphate group

BASE PAIRS

A — T

Adenine   Thymine

G — C

Guanine   Cytosine

RIBONUCLEIC ACID (RNA)

RNA is single sugar-phosphate backbone with nucleotide bases. RNA acts as a middle man molecule–taking the instructions for protein production from DNA to another part of the cell, where in accordance with the RNA instructions, amino acids are pieced together into proteins.

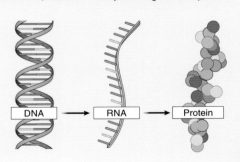

DNA → RNA → Protein

What Is LIFE? SECOND EDITION   A GUIDE TO BIOLOGY   **Jay Phelan**

2·1–2·3 Atoms form molecules through bonding.

An atom is the smallest unit into which material can be divided without losing its essential properties. Molecules are atoms linked together.

ATOM STRUCTURE

All atoms are made up of protons and neutrons in the nucleus, and electrons, which circle far around the nucleus.

CARBON ATOM

- ➕ 6 Protons
- ⬤ 6 Neutrons
- ⊖ 6 Electrons

ELECTRON SHELLS AND ATOM STABILITY

The chemical characteristics of an atom depend on the number of electrons in its outermost shell. When atoms have electron vacancies in their outermost shell, they are more likely to interact with other atoms.

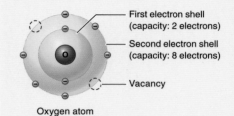

- First electron shell (capacity: 2 electrons)
- Second electron shell (capacity: 8 electrons)
- Vacancy

Oxygen atom

UNSTABLE ATOM

Vacancy

Hydrogen atom

STABLE ATOM

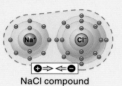

Helium atom

ATOM BONDING

Atoms can be bound together in three ways: covalent bonds, ionic bonds, and hydrogen bonds.

COVALENT BOND
A bond formed when atoms share electrons in order to become more stable, forming a molecule.

H₂ molecule

IONIC BOND
An attraction between two oppositely charged ions, forming a compound.

NaCl compound
➕⇒ ⇐➖

HYDROGEN BOND
An attraction between the slightly positively charged hydrogen atom of one molecule and the slightly negatively charged atom of another.

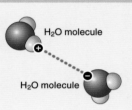

H_2O molecule

H_2O molecule

2·4–2·6 Water has features that enable it to support all life.

Water molecules easily form hydrogen bonds, giving water great cohesiveness and the ability to resist temperature changes, and making it a versatile solvent.

HYDROGEN BONDS

The hydrogen bonds between water molecules give water several of its most important characteristics that enable it to support all life.

COHESIVENESS
Hydrogen bonds cause water molecules to "stick" together, allowing trees to transport them from the soil to their leaves.

HIGH HEAT CAPACITY
Water resists heating because heat energy from the sun is used up breaking and reforming hydrogen bonds.

LOW DENSITY AS A SOLID
When frozen, water becomes less dense due to the arrangement of molecules into a crystalline lattice.

GOOD SOLVENT
Water pries apart ionic bonds, dissolving ionic compounds.

THE pH SCALE

The pH of a fluid is a measure of how acidic or basic a solution is and depends on the concentration of H^+ ions present.

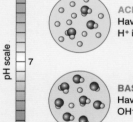

pH scale 0 — 7 — 14

ACIDS
Have a greater proportion of H^+ ions relative to OH^- ions.

BASES
Have a greater proportion of OH^- ions relative to H^+ ions.

2·7–2·10 Carbohydrates are fuel for living machines.

Carbohydrates, made up of carbon, oxygen, and hydrogen, are the primary fuel for running all cellular machinery and also form much of the structure of cells.

SIMPLE CARBOHYDRATES

The simplest carbohydrates, including glucose—the most important carbohydrate to living organisms—are monosaccharides or simple sugars. They contain from three to seven carbon atoms.

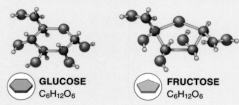

GLUCOSE
$C_6H_{12}O_6$

FRUCTOSE
$C_6H_{12}O_6$

COMPLEX CARBOHYDRATES

Multiple simple carbohydrates are sometimes linked together into more complex carbohydrates. Types of complex carbohydrates include starch, which is the primary form of energy storage in plants, and glycogen, which is a primary form of energy storage in animals. Some complex carbohydrates, including chitin and cellulose, cannot be digested by most animals.

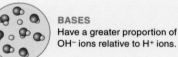

GLYCOGEN
Primary form of energy storage in animals.

STARCH
Primary form of energy storage in plants.

CHITIN
Forms the rigid outer skeleton of most insects and crustaceans.

CELLULOSE
Structural material found in plants that is indigestible by humans.

What Is LIFE? SECOND EDITION — A GUIDE TO BIOLOGY — Jay Phelan

1·14–1·17 Scientific thinking can help us make wise decisions. ◄ (continued from other side)

Visual displays of data can help readers think about and compare data, ultimately helping them to synthesize the information and see useful patterns.

COMMON ELEMENTS OF EFFECTIVE GRAPHICAL PRESENTATIONS OF DATA

Shown here: an example of a line graph.

TITLE
- Describes the content of the display

y-AXIS
- Vertical axis that presents one dimension by which the data can be described

DEPENDENT VARIABLE
- A measurable entity that is created by the process observed
- The value is expected to change in response to a change in the independent variable
- Generally represented on the y-axis

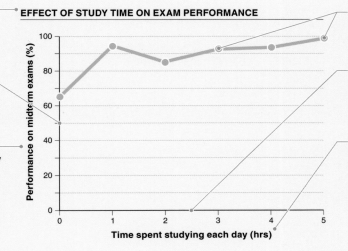

EFFECT OF STUDY TIME ON EXAM PERFORMANCE

(y-axis: Performance on midterm exams (%), ranging 0 to 100; x-axis: Time spent studying each day (hrs), ranging 0 to 5)

DATA POINTS
- Individual measurements plotted within the visual display

x-AXIS
- Horizontal axis that presents one dimension by which the data can be described

INDEPENDENT VARIABLE
- A measurable entity that is available at the start of a process
- The value can be changed as required
- Generally represented on the x-axis

STATISTICS

Statistics can quantify and summarize large amounts of data, making it possible to draw more accurate conclusions. Because much variation exists in the world, statistics can help us evaluate whether differences between a treatment group and control group can be attributed to the treatment rather than random chance.

PSEUDOSCIENCE AND ANECDOTAL OBSERVATIONS

Pseudoscience, in which individuals make scientific-sounding claims that are not supported by trustworthy, methodical scientific studies and anecdotal observations often lead people to believe that links between two phenomena exist, when there are no such links.

1·18 On the road to biological literacy: what are the major themes in biology?

Although the diversity of life on earth is tremendous, the study of life is unified by the themes of hierarchical organization and the power of evolution.

HIERARCHICAL ORGANIZATION

Life is organized on many levels within individual organisms, including atoms, cells, tissues, and organs. And in the larger world, organisms themselves are organized into many levels: populations, communities, and ecosystems within the biosphere.

THE POWER OF EVOLUTION

Evolution, the change in genetic characteristics of individuals within populations over time, accounts for the diversity of organisms, but also explains the unity among them.

What Is LIFE? SECOND EDITION

A GUIDE TO BIOLOGY

Jay Phelan

WHAT'S THIS?

When I was a student, one of my professors had a policy of allowing students to bring in a single 8 1/2" x 11" sheet of paper into our exams. We were allowed to write whatever we wanted on this page beforehand and use it during the exam. I spent hours trying to distill the course material to its essential ideas and information. I mastered the art of tiny writing. And I often produced summary documents that I was proud of.

It was with those little summaries in mind that I created the "To Go" guides. Please understand that they are not meant to be a replacement for the chapter reading or even the chapter summary. Rather, they are a prompt, to help you recall, review, and contemplate the most important material from the chapter after you have spent time reading and studying it. I hope they help you!

—Jay Phelan

1 SCIENTIFIC THINKING...*to go*

1·1–1·3 Science is a collection of facts and a process for understanding the world.

Through objective observation, description, and experimentation, science helps us to discover and better understand the world around us.

WHAT IS SCIENCE?

Science is not simply a body of knowledge or a list of facts to be remembered. It is an intellectual activity, encompassing observation, description, experimentation, and explanation of natural phenomena.

WHAT IS BIOLOGY?

Biology is the study of living things.

BIOLOGICAL LITERACY IS ESSENTIAL IN THE MODERN WORLD

Biological issues permeate all aspects of our lives. To make wise decisions, it is essential for individuals and societies to attain biological literacy.

1·4–1·10 A beginner's guide: what are the steps of the scientific method?

The scientific method is a flexible, adaptable, and efficient pathway to understanding the world.

THE SCIENTIFIC METHOD: FIVE BASIC STEPS AND ONE FLEXIBLE PROCESS

The scientific method consists of five basic steps. Once begun, though, the process doesn't necessarily continue linearly through the five steps until it is concluded.

STEP 1:
MAKE OBSERVATIONS
The scientific method begins by making observations about the world, noting patterns or cause-and-effect relationships.

STEP 2:
FORMULATE A HYPOTHESIS
A hypothesis is a proposed explanation for an observed phenomenon.

STEP 3:
DEVISE A TESTABLE PREDICTION
For a hypothesis to be useful, it must generate a testable prediction.

STEP 4:
CONDUCT A CRITICAL EXPERIMENT
A critical experiment is one that makes it possible to decisively determine whether a particular hypothesis is correct.

STEP 5:
DRAW CONCLUSIONS AND MAKE REVISIONS
Based on the results of experimental tests, we can revise a hypothesis and explain the observable world with increasing accuracy.

HYPOTHESIS VS. THEORY

• A hypothesis is a proposed explanation for a phenomenon. (And a good hypothesis leads to testable predictions.)

• A theory is an explanatory hypothesis for a phenomenon that is exceptionally well supported by the empirical data. (And can be thought of as a hypothesis that has withstood the test of time and is unlikely to be altered by any new evidence.)

1·11–1·13 Well-designed experiments are essential to testing hypotheses.

To draw clear conclusions from experiments, variables not of interest should be held constant, outcomes must be repeatable and biases should be minimized.

CONTROLLING VARIABLES

To draw clear conclusions from experiments, it is essential to hold constant all those variables we are not interested in. Control and experimental groups should differ only with respect to the treatment of interest. Differences in outcomes between the groups can then be attributed to the treatment.

REPEATABLE EXPERIMENTS

Experiments and their outcomes must be repeatable for their conclusions to be considered valid and widely accepted.

AVOIDING BIASES

Biases can influence our behavior, including our collection and interpretation of data. With careful controls, it is possible to minimize such biases.

1·14–1·17 Scientific thinking can help us make wise decisions.

(continued on other side) ▶

Visual displays of data can help readers think about and compare data, ultimately helping them to synthesize the information and see useful patterns.

COMMON VISUAL DISPLAYS OF DATA USED IN BIOLOGY

There is an almost infinite variety of ways to display data, including maps, tables, charts, and graphs. Graphs are particularly prevalent in biology, and a few forms are used most frequently.

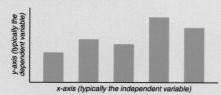  

BAR GRAPH
Rectangular bars are used to represent data, each with a height that is proportional to the value being represented.

LINE GRAPH
A line or curve may be used to connect data points or to illustrate trends across many data points.

PIE CHART
"Slices" are used to represent data, in which each slice is a proportion of the whole.

What Is LIFE? SECOND EDITION **A GUIDE TO BIOLOGY**

Jay Phelan